MOTION

Minds·On PHYSICS

Activities & Reader

MOTION

Minds·On PHYSICS

Activities & Reader

William J. Leonard
Robert J. Dufresne
William J. Gerace
Jose P. Mestre

The University of Massachusetts
Physics Education Research Group

KENDALL/HUNT PUBLISHING COMPANY
4050 Westmark Drive   Dubuque, Iowa 52002

Also available in the Minds•On Physics Series

Teacher's Guide to accompany Minds•On Physics: Motion

Minds•On Physics: Interactions / Activities & Reader

Teacher's Guide to accompany Minds•On Physics: Interactions

Minds•On Physics: Conservation Laws & Concept-Based Problem Solving / Activities & Reader

Teacher's Guide to accompany Minds•On Physics: Conservation Laws & Concept-Based Problem Solving

Available Fall 1999 from Kendall/Hunt

Minds•On Physics: Fields, Complex Systems & Other Advanced Topics / Activities & Reader

Teacher's Guide to accompany Minds•On Physics: Fields, Complex Systems & Other Advanced Topics

Author Address for Correspondence

William J. Leonard
Department of Physics & Astronomy
Box 34525
University of Massachusetts
Amherst, MA 01003–4525 USA

e-mail: WJLEONARD@phast.umass.edu

Cover Photos: Image of roller coaster "The Dragon" courtesy of Adventureland Park, Des Moines, Iowa. Tennis player image © 1997 PhotoDisc. All other images courtesy of Corel.

Copyright © 1999 by Kendall/Hunt Publishing Company

ISBN 0-7872-3927-5

This book was prepared with the support of NSF Grant: ESI 9255713. However, any opinions, findings, conclusions and or recommendations herein are those of the authors and do not necessarily reflect the views of NSF.

Printed in the United States of America
10 9 8 7 6 5 4 3 2 1

Contents

continued

Activities (continued)

Reader
Chapter 1: Describing Motion

Reader (continued)

continued

Reader (continued)

Reader (continued)

How to Use This Book

The activities in this book are designed to get you *thinking about* and *doing* physics —
in a way that is a lot closer to the way professional scientists think about and do science.
You will learn by communicating your ideas with your teacher and with other students,
and by trying to make sense of the ideas presented in the book.

During the school year, you may be required to memorize some definitions, vocabulary,
and other basic information, but you should <u>not</u> try to memorize the answers to specific
questions and problems. Answers should *make sense to you.* If they do not make sense
to you, then you probably should go back and change how you think about the
problem or situation. Even if everyone else seems to understand something, please do
not give up! Keep trying until it makes sense to you.

We want *everyone* in the class to understand physics, and we sincerely believe that
everyone *can* learn to understand physics. The activities in this book are designed to
help you *start* developing the skills needed to learn physics. *You* must do the rest. If
necessary, your teacher and your classmates should be able to help you. Find out how
they think about a problem or situation, and adapt their ideas to your own way of
thinking. And if you are helping someone else, remember that everyone learns at a
different rate, so please be patient.

This style of learning requires a lot of dedication and work, especially if you are not
familiar with the style. In the short run, this style might seem impossible and not
worth the extra effort. But in the long run, it is definitely worth it. We really, really
want you to memorize *as little as possible.* Focus on the ideas that are most widely
useful, and learn how to use these to derive the relationships you might need to answer
a question or solve a problem. You will be able to solve lots of problems using this
approach, and you will develop skills that will be useful in any field you might choose
to enter. Remember that physics is one way — among many — of looking at the
natural world. It's a way of analyzing, evaluating, describing, explaining and predicting
the behavior of objects and collections of objects.

Acknowledgments

The *concept-based problem-solving* approach to learning is the way Bill Gerace has taught hundreds of graduate and undergraduate students at the University of Massachusetts. It is his approach that has been refined, modified, and adapted to create the activities in this book.

We are deeply grateful to the National Science Foundation for funding the pilot project, *Materials for Developing Concept-Based Problem-Solving Skills in Physics*, under grant MDR–9050213. Although we had no prior experience writing materials for high-school physics, the Foundation reasoned that as experts in both physics and cognitive research, we were uniquely qualified to bring a fresh outlook to the task. We thank NSF also for funding the renewal, *Minds-On Physics: An Integrated Curriculum for Developing Concept-Based Problem Solving in Physics*, under grant ESI–9255713. The materials in this book are a direct result of this funding and are also evidence of how federal support can impact education and stimulate reform. We thank Gerhard Salinger, our project director at NSF, for his unwavering support of our approach and his many suggestions.

We are very fortunate to have found four wonderful teachers who were willing to try a different approach to teaching physics by field-testing those first 24 "modules" of the pilot project: Charlie Camp (Amherst Regional HS, Amherst, MA), Mike Cunha (Weaver HS, Hartford, CT), Steve Degon (Central HS, Springfield, MA) and Hughes Pack (Northfield–Mount Hermon School, Northfield, MA). They let us into their classrooms and let us see first-hand how their students dealt with the approach. Their numerous suggestions have improved the materials and the approach greatly.

We also thank all the teachers who have field-tested the Minds•On Physics activities: Jane Barrett (Howard School of Academics & Technology, Chattanooga, TN), Larry Blanchard (Warren Easton HS, New Orleans, LA), Roger Blough (Tyner HS, Chattanooga, TN), Gaby Blum (Monument Mountain Regional HS, Great Barrington, MA), Charlie Camp (ARHS), Jim Carter (Saugus HS, Saugus, MA), Jack Czajkowski (Pioneer Valley Regional School District, MA), John Dark (Brainerd HS, Chattanooga, TN), Steve Degon (Central HS), Ed Eckel (NMH), Jen DuBois (NMH), Jake Foster (Hixson HS, Hixson, TN), Bill Fraser (Chattanooga Phoenix School 3, Chattanooga, TN), Ken Gano (Hixson HS), Dennis Gilbert (Taconic HS, Pittsfield, MA), Craig Hefner (NMH), Ray Janke (Chicopee HS, Chicopee, MA), Aaron Kropf (ARHS), Bernie Lally (Chicopee HS), Michael Oliphant (Millis HS, Millis, MA), Hughes Pack (NMH), Jerry

Pate (Chattanooga School for Arts and Sciences, Chattanooga, TN), Kirk Rau (Tyner HS), Jessie Royal (Dade County HS, Trenton, GA), Cheryl Ryan (Hoosac Valley Regional HS, Adams, MA), John Safko (The University of South Carolina), Glenda Schmidt (Slidell HS, Slidell, LA), Lisa Schmitt (NMH), Steve Schultheis (Saugus HS), Lance Simpson (NMH), Mark Walcroft (Taconic HS), Mark Wenig (CSAS), Maxine Willis (Gettysburg HS, Gettysburg, PA), Melany O'Connor (NMH), and Tom Winn (McMain HS, New Orleans, LA). They often had little warning about what and when materials would arrive, and usually had just a few days to prepare themselves to do the activities in class. We appreciate their patience and understanding. We also thank them for recommending that we create extensive teacher support materials. Although this addition has nearly doubled the scope of the project, it is a welcome change, and every teacher who uses the Minds•On Physics materials is indebted to them.

We thank Kris Chapman and Maggie Coffin for many of the drawings used in the activities. They brought a style and grace to the figures that none of us could ever match. We thank Ian Beatty for creating the Town of King's Court. We also thank Gary Bradway (Berkshire Community College, Pittsfield, MA), for his frequent help with conceptualizing and revising the early activities; Jerry Touger (Curry College, Milton, MA), for his help writing the Reader; and George Collison (The Concord Consortium, Concord, MA), for showing us how hands-on activities may be combined with minds-on activities.

Thanks to Allan Feldman (University of Massachusetts, Amherst, MA) and the rest of his evaluation team (Karla, Jim, Ed, Sonal, and Aaron) for evaluating the materials and its implementation.

We are thankful to Kendall/Hunt for publishing these materials. We are particularly thankful to the people at K/H for their many ideas and suggestions, especially regarding the format and style of these materials.

Special thanks also to all our friends and relatives.

Bill Leonard
Bob Dufresne
Bill Gerace
Jose Mestre

The UMass Physics Education Research Group
Department of Physics & Astronomy
Box 34525
University of Massachusetts
Amherst, MA 01003–4525 USA

(Visit us on the Web at http://www-perg.phast.umass.edu/)

Activities

1-35:
MOTION

Looking Ahead

Purpose and Expected Outcome

When you begin to study something new, what you already know and how you think about the subject affects what you notice and what you learn. Sometimes what you know and think is helpful in deciding what to pay attention to and how to interpret new ideas. At other times, what you know and think can interfere with understanding new ideas. Because of this, it is a good idea to become aware of what you think about a subject before you try to make sense of the new ideas presented to you. In order to understand fully the new ideas it may be necessary for you to put aside or alter the way you think about the subject.

The first part of this course will be concerned with describing the motion of objects and understanding why objects move the way they do. Two of the most important ideas you will study are *force* and *acceleration*. The purpose of this activity is to record your initial thinking about forces and acceleration before we start to study the physics definitions of these ideas. Later on, when you have finished studying forces and acceleration, you will return to this activity to see how your ideas have changed.

Prior Experience / Knowledge Needed

No prior knowledge or experience is needed to do this activity.

Explanation of Activity

This activity has two parts. In the first part, you will consider a number of different situations and attempt to describe the forces acting on the objects in the situations. In the second part, you will predict what you believe will happen in a number of other situations. Answer the questions according to your intuition, rather than being overly concerned with getting the "correct" answer.

PART A: Analyzing the Motion of Common Objects

Below are some familiar situations. For each one, state what you believe to be the force (or forces) acting on the specified object, and indicate whether or not you think the object is accelerating.

A1. A book rests on a table.

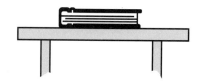

(a) List and describe the forces that you think are acting on the book.

(b) Do you think the book is accelerating? Explain.

(c) Explain why the book does not fall.

A2.

A ball is thrown straight up. Consider the ball while it is in the air (<u>after</u> it is released).

(a) List and describe the forces that you think are acting on the ball.

(b) Do you think the ball is accelerating? If so, during which parts of its motion is it accelerating? Explain.

(c) Explain why the ball moves upward and then moves downward.

A3. A chair is pushed across the floor at constant speed. Consider only when the chair is in motion.

(a) List and describe the forces that you think are acting on the chair.

(b) Do you think the chair is accelerating? Explain.

(c) Explain why the chair is moving at constant speed.

A4.

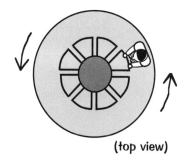

(top view)

A child is riding on a merry-go-round that is spinning very quickly at a constant rate.

(a) List and describe the forces that you think are acting on the child.

(b) Do you think the child is accelerating? Explain.

(c) Explain why the child is moving in a circle.

PART B: Predicting the Outcome of an Event

The power of physics is that it helps you to make predictions. For each situation below, (a) predict what you believe will happen, and (b) indicate how confident you are in your prediction. Use a scale of 1–5 to indicate your confidence level, where "1" means "I guessed," and "5" means "I am very, very confident." Since we have not yet presented any physics laws, do not be concerned with whether or not your answers are correct. Instead, be prepared to explain why you made the predictions you did.

B1.

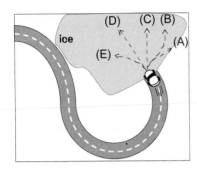

A car traveling along a curved road drives over a very slippery patch of ice as shown. When the car is on the ice it loses all traction.

(a) Which of the dashed lines at left best represents the path of the car after it goes onto the ice?

(b) How confident are you in your prediction?

B2. Two soccer balls roll toward each other at right angles and collide as shown (seen from above).

(a) After the balls collide, which dashed line best represents the path of ball #1?

(b) How confident are you in your prediction?

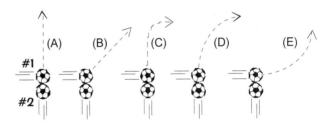

B3.

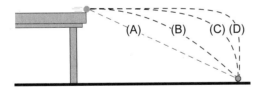

A marble rolls off the edge of a table.

(a) Which of the dashed lines best represents the path of the marble after it leaves the table?

(b) How confident are you in your prediction?

B4. A cube of metal placed on a scale registers 6lb. A wooden board placed symmetrically on two scales registers 1lb on each scale. The metal cube is moved onto the board, one-third of the way from the left end of the board.

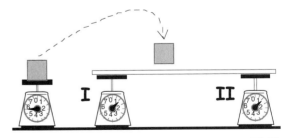

(a) What is the new reading on scale I?

(A) 1lb (B) 2lb (C) 3lb (D) 4lb (E) 5lb (F) 7lb

(b) How confident are you in your prediction?

(c) What is the new reading on scale II?

(A) 1lb (B) 2lb (C) 3lb (D) 4lb (E) 5lb (F) 7lb

(d) How confident are you in this prediction?

Reflection

R1. As you were working on part A, (a) how did you decide what forces were acting on the objects? (b) How did you decide whether or not an object was accelerating?

R2. In part B, (a) how often did you disagree with your classmates? (b) Why do you suppose your predictions differed from some of your classmates' predictions?

Integration of Ideas

Consider the following situation: Two <u>identical</u> sailboats with different colored sails are traveling to the right in still water. The positions of the sailboats at successive one-second time intervals are shown in the diagram below. You should assume that the sailboats are being pushed along by a steady wind.

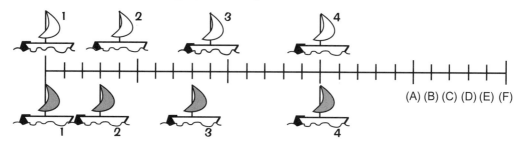

I1. Predict where each boat will be after the next time interval. Use the position of the mast as a reference.

   (a) White boat: A B C D E F   (c) Gray boat: A B C D E F

   (b) Confidence: (low) 1 2 3 4 5 (high)   (d) Confidence: (low) 1 2 3 4 5 (high)

I2. Describe the forces acting on the two sailboats.

I3. Is either sailboat accelerating? Which one? How do you know?

I4. Compare the strengths of the wind forces on the two boats by filling in the two blank spaces in the following statement:

> "The wind force on the top (white) sailboat is _____ the wind force on the bottom (gray) sailboat. The wind forces on the sailboats are _____."

      (A) greater than / not zero   (D) equal to / zero
      (B) equal to / not zero   (E) Impossible to determine
      (C) less than / not zero

Communicating the Position of an Object

Purpose and Expected Outcome

In this activity, you will learn how to communicate accurately the position of an unknown object.

Prior Experience / Knowledge Needed

No prior experience is necessary to do this activity.

Explanation of Activity

Working in a group, create a general "code" for describing the position of any object in your classroom. Your code should allow another person in your group to locate any unknown (but stationary) object or person described by the code. Without mentioning any specific objects or people in the room, your code should use the fewest possible letters and/or numbers, while still describing accurately the position of something (or someone).

After you have developed your code, one member of your group should leave the room. The teacher will then identify an object in the room and your group will describe its location using your code. The group member who previously left should now return and attempt to locate and identify the object using only the code. Do not help this person in any way! Rather, observe any difficulties he/she is having carrying out your instructions.

Materials

You may use: Rulers, Protractors, Pencils, Paper, and/or Meter Sticks to do this activity. Check with your teacher if you would like to use anything else.

Reflection

R1. What have you learned about the following ideas:

    (a) using a fixed point of reference (sometimes called the origin of the coordinate system)?

    (b) using a fixed and well defined unit of measure?

    (c) having fixed and well defined spatial directions?

    (d) having spatial directions that are perpendicular to each other?

R2. How did the requirement of creating a "minimal" code affect how you chose to communicate the location of an object? Did the language become more precise as a result or less? Did the language become more abstract or less? Did it become more symbolic or less? What standard conventions did you use?

R3. Were there any similarities in the codes that different groups created? What were some of the important differences between codes? Which code was the most efficient? Why was it the most efficient?

Communicating the Position of an Object (Alternative Version)

Purpose and Expected Outcome

In this activity, you will learn how to communicate accurately the position of an unknown object.

Prior Experience / Knowledge Needed

No prior experience is necessary to do this activity.

Explanation of Activity

Working in a group, you will create a set of written instructions that will allow someone outside your group to locate an object in the classroom.

Part A. Develop a general system of instructions that will allow <u>anyone</u> to locate and identify an object. Your system should be general enough to apply to any object, but easy for anyone to understand and apply. For example, do not use any specialized vocabulary, and do not refer to objects that might not be present when you do part B.

Part B. Pick an object at random, or have someone outside your group pick an object, and write a set of instructions explaining where the object is located. Find someone who does not know which object has been chosen, and have that person follow your directions. Is the person able to locate and identify the unknown object? What difficulties did the person have following your instructions? What should you have done differently?

Reflection

R1. What have you learned about the following ideas:

   (a) using a fixed point of reference (sometimes called the origin of the coordinate system)?

   (b) using a fixed and well defined unit of measure?

   (c) using terms and symbols that have well defined meanings, so that you are not misunderstood so easily?

   (d) having fixed and well defined spatial directions?

   (e) having spatial directions that are perpendicular to each other?

R2. What have you learned about the importance of precise communication? (or the pitfalls of imprecise communication?)

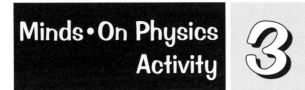
Describing Position

Purpose and Expected Outcome

In this activity, you will learn to describe the position of different objects using three different methods or *representations*. They are: (1) as a magnitude and a direction; (2) as one, two, or three *components*; and (3) as a *directed line segment* (an arrow).

Prior Experience / Knowledge Needed

You should be familiar with number lines and 2-dimensional coordinate systems. You should know the meaning of a *scale* and know how to use a scale to determine the size of something. Also, you should have been introduced to the *metric* system of units (meters, grams, kilometers, kilograms, centimeters, etc.) and its abbreviations (m, gm, km, kg, cm, etc.). Finally, keep in mind that the directed line segment for the position of an object always starts at the origin of the chosen coordinate system and ends at the object itself.

Equipment Needed

To complete this activity, you will need a protractor and a ruler marked in centimeters.

Explanation of Activity

For each of the following situations, describe the position of the objects shown. In each case, specify the position using all three representations. Use a ruler and protractor as necessary. Note that the components of the position are often called *coordinates*.

SITUATION A: One Dimension

Three cars, labeled X, Y, and Z, are traveling along a straight road as shown.

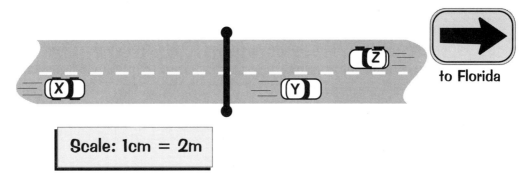

Scale: 1cm = 2m

A1. Sketch a side view of this situation. Be sure to draw all parts to scale, and include your scale in your drawing.

A2. On your drawing from A1:

(a) Choose an origin and mark it clearly.

(b) Draw directed line segments (arrows) to represent the positions of the three cars.

A3. Make a table for the positions of the three cars, as shown below, using (a) components, and (b) magnitudes and directions. (**Note:** To fill in the position of car Y we have used the black bar as the origin.)

TABLE OF POSITIONS

Representation	Position of CarX	Position of CarY	Position of CarZ
(a) Component		+3.8 m	
(b) Magnitude & Direction		3.8 m, to the right	

A4. What did you use as the origin of your coordinate system?

A5. Did you use the same origin for all 3 cars?

A6. What direction did you choose to be positive?

A7. Did you use the same positive direction for all 3 cars?

SITUATION B: Two Dimensions

Three objects are distributed on a tiled floor as shown. We have chosen the origin to be the point at which the "North" axis and the "East" axis cross each other.

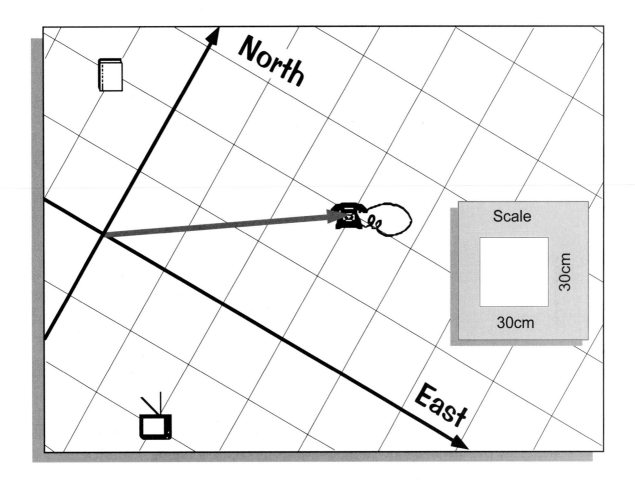

B1. Make a sketch of this situation and draw directed line segments to represent the positions of the three objects. (We have already done so for the telephone.)

B2. Using a table, specify the positions of the phone, the book, and the television set, in the other two representations (as a pair of components and as a magnitude and a direction). **Hint:** The "East" component of the television set is 60cm.

SITUATION C: Three Dimensions

A hiker is climbing up a hill. The curved "contour" lines each indicate a fixed altitude or elevation above sea level. Thus, the hill top is over 500 meters above sea level. Assume that the origin is at sea level, directly below the top of the hill.

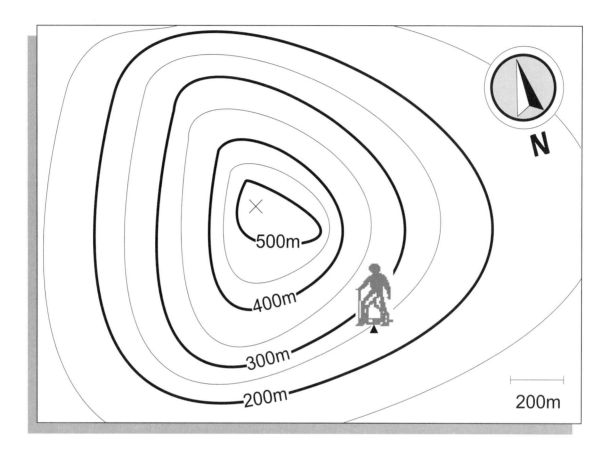

C1. Specify the coordinates of the hiker. (That is, what are the components of the hiker's position?)

C2. You cannot use the diagram to measure directly the distance from the origin to the hiker. Estimate the magnitude of the hiker's position.

C3. How would you represent the hiker's position using a directed line segment?

Reflection

R1. (a) How many components did you use for each of the 3 situations?

(b) Did the number of components always equal the number of dimensions? Why or why not?

R2. You are trying to explain to a friend the location of your house. Which representation (component, magnitude & direction, directed line segment, or some other) would you use? Of the three representations used in this activity, which is most similar to the one used to locate your house? In what sense are they different?

R3. Sometimes the location of a major city is described using a latitude and a longitude. Which representation (component, magnitude & direction, or directed line segment) is most similar to "latitude & longitude"? Explain.

Integration of Ideas

Consider the following drawing of different people, animals, and items found in a park, and answer the questions below. As in situation B, the origin has already been chosen.

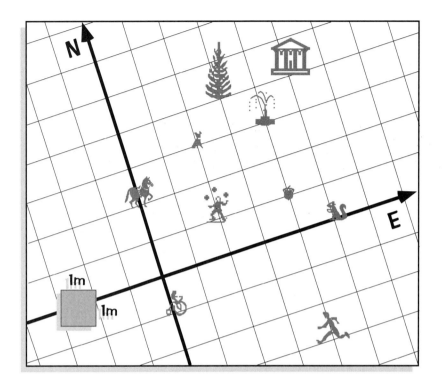

I1. Which person, animal, or item is located closest to the point (4m E, 3m N)?

I2. (a) Which object (or objects) could be described by the coordinates (d E, 0 N)?

(b) Estimate d for each of these objects.

I3. Four objects are equidistant from the origin. Which four?

I4. Which object is closest to 35° N of E?

I5. Which object is farthest from the origin?

I6. Which object is closest to the point (2cm E, 1cm N)?

I7. Which two objects are farthest apart from each other?

Using Graphs of Position vs. Time

Purpose and Expected Outcome

Having analyzed the position of objects in one, two, and three dimensions, we would now like to represent the <u>motion</u> of objects. To do this, we consider objects moving in a straight line and plot the (one-dimensional) position versus time. After doing this activity, you will know how to interpret position vs. time graphs.

Prior Experience / Knowledge Needed

You should be familiar with the coordinate (component) representation of position in one dimension.

Explanation of Activity and Examples

There are two parts in this activity.

PART A: Reading and Interpreting Graphs of Position

Below are shown the position versus time graphs for three different objects. Assume that all three objects begin their motion at $t = 0$ seconds. Answer the following questions about the motion of the objects. In some cases, you will be asked to explain your answers.

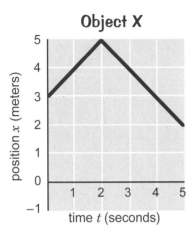

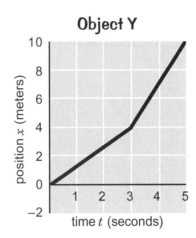

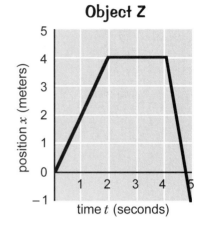

E1. When is Object Y six meters away from the origin?

Answer: *Object Y is 6 meters from the origin at about $t = 3^1/_2$ seconds.*

E2. Which object is at $x = 2$ meters first?

Answer: *Object Z is 2 meters from the origin first, arriving at about $t = 1s$.*

A1. How far is Object Z from the origin at $t = 3$ seconds?

A2. Which object takes the least time to reach a position 4 meters from the origin?

A3. Which object is farthest from the origin at $t = 2$ seconds?

A4. Is there an object that eventually returns to the origin and, if so, which one does this and when does this occur?

A5. What is the total <u>distance</u> traveled by each of the 3 objects during the full 5-second time interval? Explain.

A6. Which object has the largest <u>displacement</u> (change in position) between $t = 1$ second and $t = 3$ seconds? Explain.

A7. Which object has the largest displacement during the full 5 seconds? Explain.

16

Activity 4
Using Graphs of Position vs. Time

PART B: Associating Motion with Graphs of Position vs. Time

For each description of a physical situation, (a) identify which of the graphs below <u>could</u> represent the motion of the object; and (b) indicate how the variable x relates to the physical situation. In some cases, you should specify which direction is positive before choosing a graph. (**Note**: For some situations, more than one graph is acceptable.)

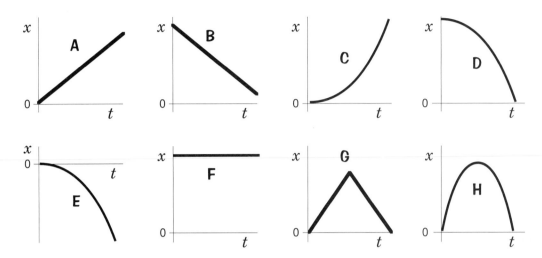

> **E3.** A ball is dropped from a height of 1 meter above the floor. Take the origin to be at the level of the floor.
>
> **Answer:** *For "up" chosen to be the positive direction, graph D would represent the motion of the ball.*
>
> **Explanation:** *The variable x represents the height of the ball above the floor. This height starts at 1 meter at t = 0s and diminishes to zero at a later time. Graph E is incorrect because the graph does not start at x = 1m. Graph B qualitatively describes the motion since the graph starts at positive x and diminishes.*

B1. A marble is rolled at constant speed along a horizontal surface toward the origin. The marble is released at a distance of 1 meter away from the origin.

B2. A block sits at rest on a table 1 meter above the floor. Take the origin to be the level of the floor.

B3. A ball is dropped from a height of 2 meters above the floor. Take the origin to be the point from which the ball is released.

B4. A ball is rolled along a horizontal surface. The ball strikes a wall and rebounds toward the origin.

B5. A car is parked on a steep hill.

Reflection

R1. Define what is meant by the expressions "origin of a coordinate system", "origin of a graph", and "original position of an object". How are they similar? How are they different? Which objects (in parts A and B) have the origin as its original position?

R2. Can the "distance traveled" by an object ever be zero? How? Is there any time interval (in part A) for which any of the objects traveled zero distance? Which object, and what interval?

R3. Can the "displacement" of an object ever be zero? How? For a particular time interval beginning at $t = 0$s, Object A (in Part A) has zero displacement. What is the ending time of this interval?

R4. Which graph (in part B) represents a stationary object? Explain how you know the object is stationary.

18

Activity 4
Using Graphs of Position vs. Time

Generating Sketches
of Position vs. Time

Purpose and Expected Outcome

In this activity, you will learn how to create your own sketches of position versus time for one-dimensional motion.

Prior Experience / Knowledge Needed

You should be familiar with position versus time plots for motion in a straight line.

Explanation of Activity and Example

(a) Sketch the position vs. time graph for the motion described during the specified time interval, and (b) label the regions and critical points of your sketch according to what is happening during the time interval. (c) Sketch the situation and indicate the path of the object, the origin of your coordinate system, and the "positive" direction.

Example. A marble rolls across a table top. Take the origin to be the original position of the marble. (a) Plot the position of the marble vs. time while it is on the table. (b) Indicate the time at which the marble is at the middle of the table. (c) Sketch the path of the marble. On your sketch, indicate the origin of your coordinate system and the direction you chose to be positive.

Answer: The labeled graph of position vs. time is shown on the left below. The labeled sketch of the situation is shown on the right.

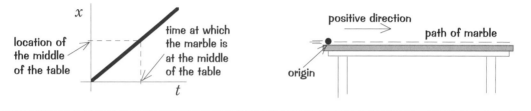

A1. You throw a ball straight upward into the air.

(a) Sketch the position vs. time graph of the ball from the time just after the ball leaves your hand until the time just before it returns to your hand. Take the origin to be the point of release of the ball, and "up" to be positive.

(b) Indicate on your graph the time at which the ball leaves your hand, the time it reaches its maximum height, and the time it returns to your hand.

(c) Sketch the path of the ball. On your sketch, indicate the origin, the positive direction, and the maximum height of the ball.

A2. A woman drives her car to a store that is located straight down a road from her home. She parks, makes a purchase, and returns home.

(a) Using her home as the origin, plot the position vs. time of the car from the time the woman leaves home until she returns.

(b) Indicate the time interval she is going <u>to</u> the store, the interval she is <u>in</u> the store, and the interval she is traveling back home.

(c) Make a sketch of the situation and on it, indicate the origin and the direction you chose to be positive.

continued

20

Activity 5
Generating Sketches of Position vs. Time

A3. A toy car is attached to a rubber band. The other end of the band is attached to the floor at some point (the origin). The rubber band is stretched horizontally until the car is 50cm from the origin, and released.

(a) Plot the position of the car from the time it is released until it reaches the origin.

(b) On your plot, indicate the time at which the car is at the origin.

(c) Sketch this situation and indicate the origin and the positive x direction.

A4. A mass M hangs from a vertical spring as shown. The mass is pulled down until the spring is extended 10cm and then released at $t = 0$s.

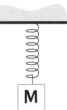

(a) Plot the vertical position of the mass from the time of release until it returns to the point of release.

(b) On your plot, indicate the times at which you believe the mass is moving the fastest.

(c) On a sketch of this situation, indicate the origin and the direction of increasing x.

A5. A marble rolls up an incline, stops, and rolls back down. Take the origin to be the point at which the marble stops rolling.

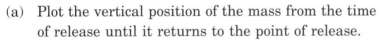

(a) Plot the position of the marble.

(b) On your plot, indicate the time interval during which it is going up the incline, and the interval during which it is going down.

(c) On a sketch of this situation, indicate the origin and the direction you chose to be "increasing x".

A6. A sprinter is running a 100-meter race indoors. She reaches her maximum speed about half-way through the race and maintains this speed until reaching the finish line. She then slows down and eventually stops herself by running into a padded wall 20 meters past the finish line.

(a) Plot the sprinter's position from the start of the race until she hits the padded wall.

(b) Label your plot.

(c) Sketch this situation. On your sketch, indicate your choice of origin and your choice for the positive direction.

Reflection

R1. Consider the slopes of your position vs. time plots.

   (a) When the object is moving in the positive direction, is the slope positive, negative, or zero?

   (b) When the object is at rest, is the slope positive, negative, or zero?

   (c) How about when the object is moving in the negative direction?

R2. (a) What can you say about the slope of x vs. t when an object is moving away from the origin? Explain.

   (b) What about when the object is moving toward the origin? Explain.

22

Activity 5
Generating Sketches of Position vs. Time

Translating Graphs of Position vs. Time

Purpose and Expected Outcome

This is the last activity that deals directly with understanding position versus time plots. In later activities, you will actually use what you have learned in order to describe accurately the motion of objects, to check your answers to questions, and to solve problems. This activity should solidify your grasp of position as it changes with time.

Prior Experience / Knowledge Needed

You should be familiar with position versus time plots for motion in a straight line.

Explanation of Activity

Using common classroom items (e.g., rubber or steel balls, springs, rubber bands, ramps, and carts), make some object move in a manner that qualitatively agrees with each of the following graphs. For each (a) briefly describe how you accomplished this, noting the location of the origin; and (b) label the time intervals and critical points of the graphs (as shown already in A1).

A1. What object did you choose to move as the graph indicates? How did you make it move like the graph? Explain.

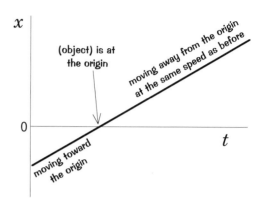

A2. (a) Which object did you make move like the graph? How did you do it?

(b) On a copy of the graph, label the various time intervals. In particular, what is happening to the object during the curved part of the graph? What is happening during the horizontal part?

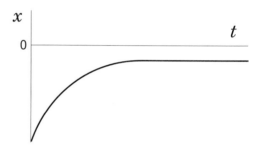

A3. (a) Describe how you made something move like this graph.

(b) Label a copy of the graph.

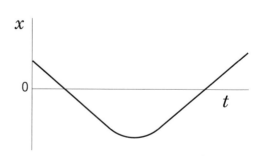

continued

24

Activity 6
Translating Graphs of Position vs. Time

A4. (a) Describe how you made an object move like this graph.

(b) Label a copy of the graph.

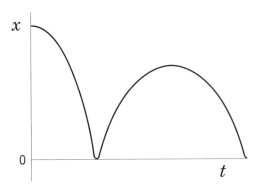

A5. (a) What object did you make move like this graph? Describe how you did it.

(b) Label a copy of the graph.

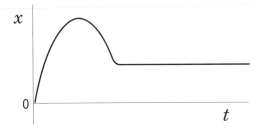

A6. (a) What object did you make move like this graph? Describe how you did it.

(b) Label a copy of the graph.

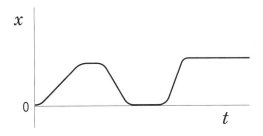

Reflection

R1. In the last three activities, we have been concerned <u>only</u> with motion in one dimension. Consider this latest activity. Was the motion of each object always in a straight line? If not, why not? How would you change your physical situations so that each moved in a straight line?

R2. Soon, we will start learning about objects moving in 2 dimensions. How would you represent motion in 2 dimensions? Could you use position vs. time graphs? If so, how many graphs would you need? How would you represent motion in 3 dimensions? How many graphs would you need then?

Integration of Ideas

Shown below is the position vs. time graph of a marble rolling along the floor. It starts at $x = 1$m at $t = 0$s and rolls in the positive direction at constant speed. (a) On the same diagram, sketch the position vs. time graphs for each of the situations described; and (b) label each sketch with a short description of the speed and direction of the marble. (For instance, I1 would read "same speed, same direction".)

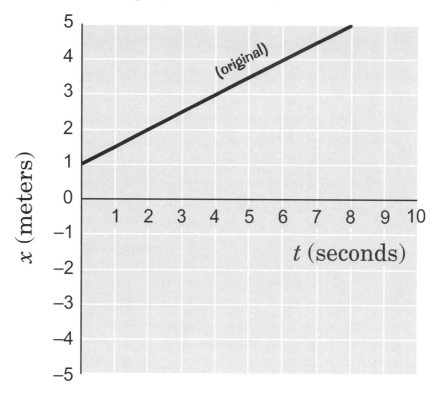

I1. A marble rolls in the same direction and with the same speed as the original, but starts at the origin instead.

I2. A marble rolls in the opposite direction with the same speed, starting at $x = 0$m.

I3. A marble has the same starting point and direction as the original, but is rolling at a faster speed (than the original).

I4. A marble starts at $x = 1$m and rolls with the same speed and direction as the original, but starts moving at $t = 4$s instead.

I5. A marble is stationary at $x = 1$m.

I6. A marble starts at the origin, and travels at a smaller speed than the original in the opposite direction.

Describing Displacement

Purpose and Expected Outcome

Eventually, we would like to use the concept of *force* to explain the motion and behavior of objects around us. Forces cause acceleration, which you can recognize by noticing changes in velocity. Velocities are defined in terms of changes in position. This is why we introduce the idea of *displacement*. Knowledge of the absolute position of an object is often less important than knowledge of the object's <u>change</u> in position. *Displacement* is the term we use to identify changes in position. In this activity, you will learn about displacement in two dimensions.

Prior Experience / Knowledge Needed

You should understand the three representations of position in two dimensions: (1) as a pair of components; (2) as a magnitude and a direction; and (3) as a directed line segment. You should know that the *displacement* is defined to be the *change in position*.

Explanation of Activity

There are two situations to consider in this activity. In the first, you will use displacements in different representations to locate different buildings. In the second situation, you are given a set of movements of a ship, and you will describe its displacements using all three representations.

SITUATION A: Riding a Bike around Town

Jasmine is riding her bike around town. She leaves her house at 1:00 PM to go to her friend Kiesha's house, but her bicycle isn't working quite right, so she goes to the bike shop, located 2 km east and 3 km south of her (own) house. After getting her bike fixed, she goes to Kiesha's house, which is located 5 km from the bike shop in a direction 20° south of west. Later in the afternoon, she leaves Kiesha's house and goes to the store to buy some milk before returning home. Her displacement from Kiesha's to the store is shown as a directed line segment in the diagram at right.

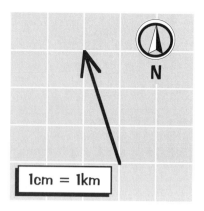

1cm = 1km

A1. On a sketch of the situation, indicate the locations of (a) the bike shop, (b) the store, and (c) Jasmine's home.

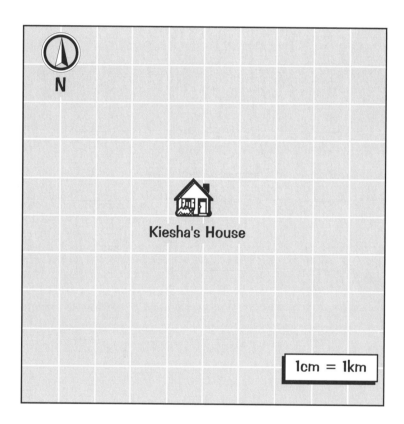

Kiesha's House

1cm = 1km

A2. What is Jasmine's displacement during the afternoon? Explain your answer.

A3. Estimate how many total kilometers Jasmine rode her bike during the afternoon. Explain how you made your estimate. How good do you suppose your estimate is?

SITUATION B: Sailing along a Coast Line

A ship moves along the coast line from its original position shown on the map (point X) to Lighthouse Bay (point Z). Along the way the ship stops for an hour near a beach located at point Y.

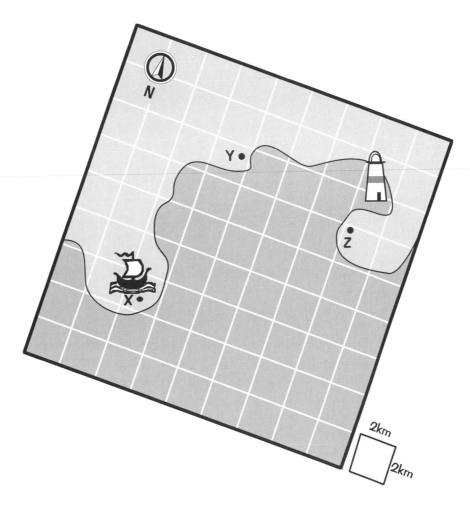

B1. On a sketch of this situation, draw directed line segment to represent the following displacements:

  (a) X to Y,

  (b) Y to Z, and

  (c) X to Z. (This is called the *net displacement*.)

B2. In a table, describe the same three displacements of the ship using (a) a pair of components, and (b) as a magnitude and a direction.

B3. Estimate the total distance traveled by the ship, and compare it to the magnitude of the *net displacement* (X to Z). Describe your method for estimating the total distance traveled.

Reflection

R1. Under what conditions is the total distance traveled during a trip equal to the magnitude of the net displacement?

R2. When the total distance and the magnitude of the net displacement are not equal, is either one always larger than the other? Which one (is always larger than the other)? Explain.

R3. Under what conditions is the net displacement equal to zero?

R4. Consider the directed line segment representation. Do all positions start at the same point? What do we call this point? Do all displacement vectors start at the same point? Explain.

Describing Velocity

Purpose and Expected Outcome

The purpose of this activity is to help you understand what a physicist means by velocity. After completing this activity you will be able to describe the velocity of objects using the three representations: component, magnitude & direction, and directed line segment. You will also be able to distinguish between position, displacement, and velocity.

Prior Experience / Knowledge Needed

You should be familiar with position and displacement in one and two dimensions. You should know that velocity is a quantity having both a speed (magnitude) and a direction. The velocity is calculated by the change in position (displacement) during a time interval divided by the length of the time interval.

Explanation of Activity

On the following pages are strobe diagrams showing the motion of different people and objects. With each strobe diagram you will be asked to describe the velocity using one or more of the three representations: component, magnitude and direction, and directed line segment. You will also be asked questions that require you to interpret the motion presented in the strobe diagrams.

PART A: Reasoning about Velocity using Directed Line Segments

A ball is thrown as shown in the strobe diagram below. The location of the ball is shown at 0.2-second time intervals. Also, a representation of the velocity **v** at point A is shown using a directed line segment. (The direction of the arrow shows the direction of motion.)

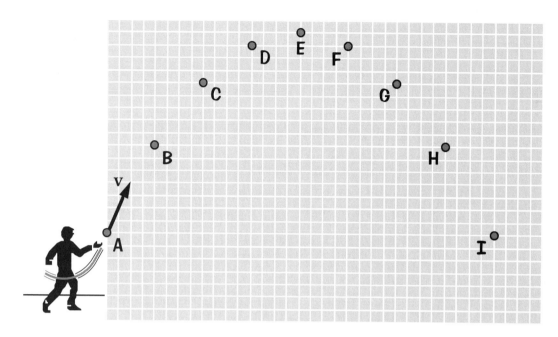

A1. On a sketch of this situation, draw directed line segments to represent the velocity of the ball at the points labeled C, E, and H.

A2. How long after being thrown does the ball arrive at location F?

A3. At which location(s) is the <u>speed</u> of the ball the largest? Explain your answer.

A4. At which location(s) is the ball moving only horizontally?

A5. When the ball is at location B,
  (a) <u>Estimate</u> the direction (angle with respect to the horizontal) that the ball is moving.
  (b) Is this angle smaller than, larger than, or the same as the angle for its velocity at A?
  (c) In what way does this angle change as the ball goes from A to E?

A6. At which location(s) is the speed of the ball the smallest? Explain.

PART B: Representing and Distinguishing Position, Displacement, and Velocity

Three women are running warm-up sprints during track practice. The strobe diagram shows the three women at four successive two-second intervals. Position A represents the location of runner A at $t = 0$s; A' represents her location at $t = 2$s; etc.

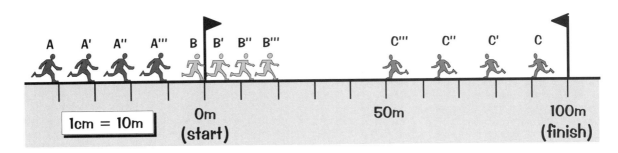

Specify each of the following quantities in each of the three representations. Use a scale of 1 centimeter (1cm) = 10 meters (10m) for distances and a scale of 1 centimeter (1cm) = 3 meters per second (3m/s) for velocities. Also, always use "to the right" as the positive direction. (Some answers have been filled in.)

REPRESENTATION

	Component	Magnitude & Direction	Directed Line Segment (1cm = 10m or 3m/s)
B1. Using the Start as the origin, specify the position of runner B at $t = 4$s.			→ 1cm
B2. Using the 50-meter marker as the origin, specify the position of runner C at $t = 2$s.		30m, to the right	
B3. Specify the displacement of runner A between the first and third strobe pictures.	+20m		
B4. Specify the displacement of runner C between $t = 0$s and $t = 4$s.			
B5. Specify the velocity of runner B. (**Note:** You should use a scale of 1cm = 3m/s.)		about 3.3m/s, to the right	
B6. Specify the velocity of runner C when she is located at the 80-meter marker.			← 2.2cm

Reflection

R1. In part A, how did the direction of the velocity change as time progressed? How did the speed change?

R2. (a) In part B, which questions <u>required</u> a well defined origin to answer?

(b) Of position, displacement, and velocity, which quantities require a well defined origin? Which quantities do <u>not</u>?

(c) Of position, displacement, and velocity, which quantities stay the same when the origin is moved?

Using Graphs of Velocity vs. Time

Purpose and Expected Outcome

This is the next in a series of activities designed to help you to develop an understanding of velocity. Previously, the motion of objects was represented with graphs of position vs. time. Then, we used strobe diagrams. Now, we introduce graphs of velocity vs. time. After completing this activity you should be able to interpret graphical sketches of the velocity of an object as a function of time as the object moves in <u>one</u> dimension.

Prior Experience / Knowledge Needed

As stated earlier, *kinematics* is concerned with the <u>description</u> of motion (with emphasis on the word description). Kinematics cannot be used to explain <u>why</u> objects behave as they do. Such an explanation requires physical laws. Again, kinematics is merely a set of defined quantities and the mathematical relationships among these quantities. Previously, we defined the position of an object and learned how to draw and interpret a plot of the position as a function of time. The next step in developing kinematics is to define *speed* and *velocity* and to understand how velocity is related to position. We start with motion in a straight line.

Explanation of Activity and Examples

There are two parts to this activity. First, you will be given graphs of velocity vs. time for 3 objects and asked some questions about them. Then, you will be given 8 sketches of velocity vs. time and asked which correspond to different physical situations.

PART A: Reading and Interpreting Graphs of Velocity vs. Time

Below are shown the velocity vs. time graphs for three different objects. In this activity you are asked to read and compare information obtained from these graphs. Assume that all of the objects begin their motion at $t = 0$s.

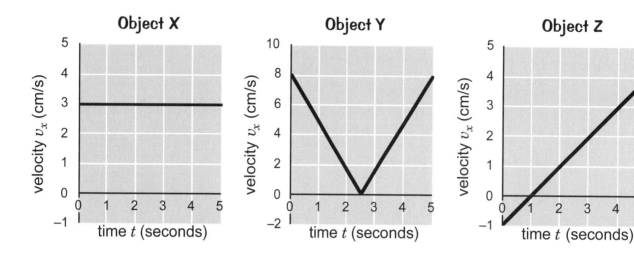

E1. When does Object Y have a velocity of 4cm/s?

Answer: Object Y has a velocity of 4cm/s first at about $t = 1^1/_4$ seconds and again at about $t = 3^3/_4$ seconds.

E2. Which object has the smallest initial speed?

Answer: Object Z has the smallest initial speed, which is 1cm/s.

A1. What is the velocity of Object Z at $t = 3$ seconds?

A2. Which object reaches a velocity of 2cm/s first?

A3. Which object has the greatest change in speed during the first 2 seconds?

A4. (a) Which object reverses direction and starts to return to its original position?
(b) When does this occur?

A5. Which of the objects are ever at rest and when does it occur?

A6. How long does it take Object X to travel 6cm?

36

Activity 9
Using Graphs of Velocity vs. Time

PART B: Associating Motion with Graphs of Velocity vs. Time

In this activity you are asked to recognize and associate graphs of velocity vs. time with the physical motion of objects in several different ways. Identify which of the graphs below could represent the motion of the object in each physical situation described. If necessary, specify which direction is positive.

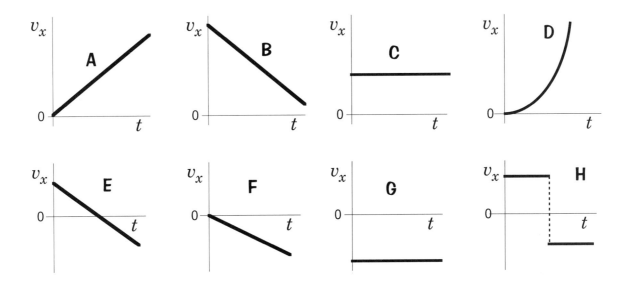

> **E3.** A marble rolls at constant speed along a horizontal surface away from the origin.
>
> **Answer:** *If it is rolling toward the positive x direction the answer is graph C. Graph G is appropriate if it is rolling toward the negative x direction.*

B1. A block is dropped from rest from a height of 1 meter above the floor. Take the origin to be at the level of the floor.

B2. A marble is released from the top of an inclined plane. Assume that positive x is measured down the plane.

B3. A ball is thrown straight up into the air. Take the origin to be at the level of the floor.

B4. A ball rolls along a horizontal surface without changing speed. The ball strikes a wall and rebounds toward the origin at approximately the same speed as before.

B5. A marble rolls onto a piece of felt, eventually stopping.

Reflection and Integration of Ideas

R1. In Part A, one of the graphs of velocity vs. time <u>looks</u> like an object bouncing off a wall, but it is not. Which object?

R2. In fact, object Y does not reverse direction at all. It moves in the positive direction and slows down until it stops. Then it speeds up, going in the same direction as before. Give an example of an everyday occurrence described by graph Y.

R3. It is easy to confuse graphs of position vs. time and velocity vs. time. In the future, we will consider both types of plots, so you must pay attention to <u>both</u> axis labels (in this case, v_x and t) in order to understand what the plot is telling you. Which questions did you answer using position vs. time graphs instead of velocity vs. time graphs?

R4. Which questions in this activity did you answer thinking that the curves "looked" like the motion of the object? How do your answers change now that you know what to look for?

38

Activity 9
Using Graphs of Velocity vs. Time

Generating Sketches of Velocity vs. Time

Purpose and Expected Outcome

In this activity, you will learn how to make your own sketches of velocity vs. time for objects moving in one dimension.

Prior Experience / Knowledge Needed

You should be familiar with velocity vs. time plots for motion in a straight line.

Explanation of Activity

(a) Sketch the velocity vs. time for the motion described, and (b) label the critical points and time intervals of your sketch. (c) On a drawing of the physical situation, specify the origin of the coordinate system and indicate the positive direction. (See Activity 5 for examples of what is meant by "labeling a graph".)

A1. You are pushing a box along the floor in the positive direction. At $t = 0$s you stop pushing the box.

  (a) Sketch the velocity of the box from the $t = 0$s until <u>after</u> it comes to rest.

  (b) Label your sketch. In particular, indicate the time at which you let go of the box and the time at which the box stops.

  (c) Make a drawing of this situation and indicate the origin and the positive direction.

A2. A woman drives her car from her home to a store which is located straight down a road from her home. She parks and makes a purchase and then returns home.

  (a) Using her home as the origin, plot the velocity of the car from the time the woman leaves home until she returns.

  (b) Label your sketch.

  (c) Draw this situation and indicate the path of the car, the origin of your coordinate system, and the direction you chose to be positive.

A3. A toy car is attached to a rubber band. The other end of the band is attached to the floor at some point (the origin). The rubber band is stretched horizontally until the car is 50 centimeters from the origin, and released.

  (a) Plot the velocity of the car from the time it is released until it reaches the origin.

  (b) Label your plot.

  (c) Make a diagram of this situation and indicate the origin and the direction of "increasing x".

continued

40

Activity 10
Generating Sketches of Velocity vs. Time

A4. A marble rolls up an incline, stops, and rolls back down the incline. Take the origin to be the point at which the marble stops rolling.

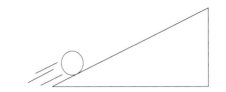

   (a) Sketch the velocity of the marble.

   (b) Label your sketch.

   (c) Make a diagram and indicate the origin and the direction you chose to be "increasing x".

A5. A sprinter is running a 100-meter race indoors. She reaches her maximum speed about half-way through the race and maintains this speed until reaching the finish line. She then slows down and eventually stops herself by running into a padded wall 20 meters past the finish line.

   (a) Plot the sprinter's velocity from the time the race begins until she has stopped again.

   (b) Label your plot. In particular, indicate the time period she is speeding up, the time she finishes the race, and the time at which she hits the padded wall.

   (c) Draw the race track. In particular, indicate the location of the starting point, the finish line, the padded wall, and the origin of your coordinate system. Also, indicate the direction you chose to be positive.

A6. A mass M hangs from a vertical spring as shown. The mass is pulled down until the spring is extended 10cm and then released at $t = 0$s.

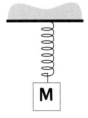

   (a) Plot the velocity of the mass from $t = 0$s until it returns to the point of release.

   (b) Label your plot.

   (c) Make a sketch of this situation and indicate the origin and the direction of increasing x.

Reflection

R1. (a) What does a negative velocity mean?

   (b) Describe a situation in which the velocity of something is negative.

R2. What does it mean when the velocity changes from positive to negative or from negative to positive?

R3. In situation A4 (the marble rolling up the incline), how long do you suppose the marble was at rest at the top of the incline?

R4. Which situation(s) has a velocity vs. time graph that is <u>qualitatively</u> like the velocity vs. time graph of a ball thrown straight up into the air?

42

Activity 10
Generating Sketches of Velocity vs. Time

Translating Graphs of Velocity vs. Time

Purpose and Expected Outcome

After doing this activity, you should be able to associate the motion of objects with graphs of velocity vs. time.

Prior Experience / Knowledge Needed

You should be familiar with velocity vs. time plots and recognize that they are different than position vs. time plots.

Explanation of Activity

(a) Using common classroom items (e.g., rubber or steel balls, springs, ramps, and carts), make some object move in a manner that is qualitatively in agreement with the following graphs. (b) Write an explanation of how you accomplished this, noting the location of your origin and the orientation of your x-axis. (c) Label the critical points and time intervals of the graphs.

A1. (a) What object did you choose to make move like this graph?

(b) Describe how you did it.

(c) On a copy of this graph, label the critical time periods. In particular, what is happening while the graph is horizontal at the beginning? at the end? What is happening while the graph is at an angle?

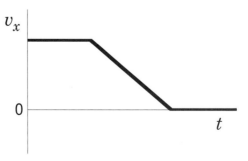

continued

A2. (a) What object did you use for this graph?

(b) How did you do it?

(c) Describe what is happening during time periods I, II, and III.

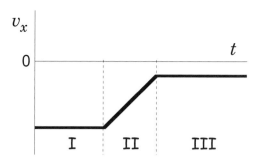

A3. (a) What object did you use for this graph?

(b) How did you do it?

(c) Describe what is happening during time periods I, II, and III.

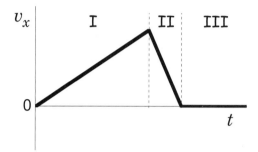

A4. (a) What object did you use for this graph?

(b) How did you do it?

(c) Make a sketch of this graph and label it.

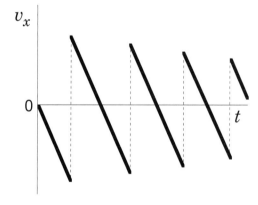

A5. (a) What object did you use for this graph?

(b) How did you do it?

(c) Label a copy of this graph. In particular, indicate the times at which the object is at rest.

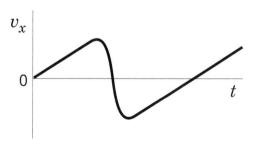

44

Activity 11
Translating Graphs of Velocity vs. Time

Integration of Ideas

Consider the graph of velocity vs. time at the right, and use this graph to answer the following questions:

I1. During which time intervals (I, II, III, or IV) is the speed of the object decreasing?

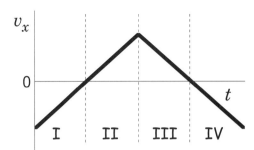

I2. During which time intervals is the speed increasing?

I3. During which time intervals is the object moving in the positive direction?

I4. During which time intervals is the object moving in the negative direction?

I5. During which time intervals is v_x increasing?

I6. Make a table indicating the <u>sign of the slope</u> of v_x vs. t in each of the situations described below. (Use + to indicate a positive slope, 0 to indicate a zero slope, and – to indicate a negative slope. Some answers have been provided.)

How the speed is changing	Sign of slope when direction of motion is positive.	Sign of slope when direction of motion is negative.
Speed is increasing. (Object is speeding up.)	+	
Speed is not changing. (Speed is constant.)		0
Speed is decreasing. (Object is slowing down.)		

I7. Can the slope of velocity vs. time be negative even though the object is speeding up? Explain. Give an example.

I8. Can the slope of velocity vs. time be positive even though the object is slowing down? Explain. Give at least one example.

Reflection

R1. Consider questions I2 and I5 of the Integration of Ideas. Are the time intervals during which the speed is increasing the same as the time intervals during which v_x is increasing? Explain.

R2. (a) If an object is slowing down, in what direction does its change in velocity point? Explain.

(b) If an object is speeding up, in what direction does its change in velocity point? Explain.

R3. (a) If the slope of velocity vs. time is positive, is the change in velocity positive or negative? Explain.

(b) If the slope of velocity vs. time is negative, is the change in velocity positive or negative? Explain.

R4. Can the slope of velocity vs. time <u>always</u> help you determine if something is slowing down or speeding up? What additional information do you need to determine if it is slowing down or not?

46

Activity 11
Translating Graphs of Velocity vs. Time

12

Relating Strobe Diagrams to Plots of Position vs. Time and Velocity vs. Time

Purpose and Expected Outcome

We have been using strobe diagrams and graphs of position and velocity versus time to represent the motion of objects. Strobe diagrams are a convenient way of picturing the actual motion of an object, by showing the object's position at fixed time intervals (for example, every 0.2 second, or every 1 second). A graph is a more abstract way to represent the motion of objects. However, the graph is a very simple and efficient way to communicate and store information about the motion of objects. It is important that you feel comfortable with both ways of representing the motion of objects. After completing this module you will be able to construct graphs of position vs. time and velocity vs. time from a strobe diagram. You will be able to describe how various features of the strobe diagram relate to features of graphs.

Prior Experience / Knowledge Needed

You should be comfortable with plots of position vs. time and velocity vs. time for objects moving along a straight line. You should be able to calculate the slope of a straight line. One of the most important features of a strobe diagram is that the time interval between successive "strobes" is the <u>same</u> throughout the diagram. Also, you need to know that the average velocity for a time interval is simply the displacement during that time interval divided by the length of the time interval. (That is, $v_{x,\text{ave}} = \Delta x/\Delta t$.)

Explanation of Activity

Shown below are strobe diagrams for three situations. First, you will be asked questions to make sure you understand the strobe diagram. Then you will make sketches of x vs. t and v_x vs. t, and relate them to the strobe diagram.

SITUATION A: Motion of a Dynamics Cart

A dynamics cart with a spring attached at one end rolls across the floor, bounces off a wall, and rolls back toward its starting point. The time sequence of the positions is indicated by the numerals 1 through 8 in the strobe diagram below. The time between each pair of strobes is 0.5 seconds. At all times, use the rear wheel of the cart to specify its position, and assume that $t = 0$s when the first strobe is taken.

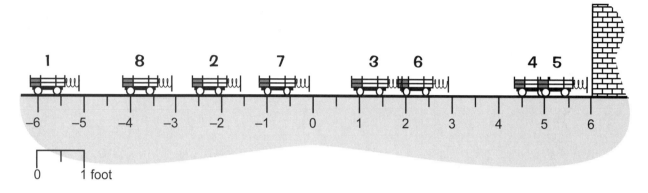

A1. Where is the cart (a) at $t = 1$s? (b) at $t = 3$s?

A2. In what direction is the cart moving (a) at $t = 0.5$s? (b) at $t = 2$s?

A3. Plot the position vs. time for the cart (using the rear wheel as the reference point) and join your points using a dotted line. Be sure to clearly label your axes.

A4. Sketch the velocity vs. time graph for the cart. Again, be sure to label both axes clearly.

A5. Approximately where is the dynamics cart at $t = 4$s? (That is, if the strobe diagram had continued, what would be the location of the 9th strobe?) Explain your prediction.

A6. How would you determine the slope of the position vs. time plot using only the strobe diagram? Explain.

A7. Describe what happens to (a) the strobe diagram, (b) the position vs. time graph, and (c) the velocity vs. time graph, when the cart collides with the wall. In particular, when does the cart hit the wall, and do all three drawings agree?

A8. How does the slope of your position vs. time graph at a certain instant relate to your estimate of the velocity at the same instant?

48

Activity 12
Relating Strobe Diagrams to Plots of Position vs. Time and Velocity vs. Time

SITUATION B: Motion of a Falling Marble

A marble is dropped from a height of 2 meters, starting from rest. The strobe diagram for this situation is shown to the right.

B1. Estimate the time interval between successive strobes. What assumptions did you make? (There are many ways to make this estimate. For example, consider how long it takes an object to fall 2 meters starting from rest.)

B2. Sketch the position vs. time graph for the marble.

B3. Sketch the velocity vs. time graph for the marble.

B4. About when is the marble at the midpoint of the 2-meter stick? Explain how you made your estimate.

B5. During which time interval is the average velocity of the marble largest in magnitude? Explain.

B6. Describe the features of (a) the strobe diagram, (b) your position vs. time graph, and (c) your velocity vs. time graph, that help you the most in deciding when the average velocity is largest.

SITUATION C: Motion of a Toy Car

A girl winds up a toy car and places it on the floor. When she releases the car, it moves as shown in the strobe diagram. The car is shown at 2-second intervals.

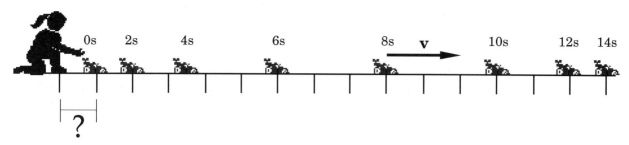

C1. Estimate the distance scale of the diagram above. That is, 1cm = ? Explain how you made your estimate.

C2. Sketch the position vs. time graph for the toy car.

C3. Sketch the velocity vs. time graph for the toy car.

C4. On a strobe diagram for the car, draw arrows to represent the <u>velocity</u> of the car at the instants shown. (The velocity at t = 8s has been drawn already. Use it as a guide to draw the other arrows.)

C5. What is the car's average velocity between t = 6s and t = 10s?

C6. (a) Estimate the location of the car at t = 7s. Explain.
(b) About where is the car at t = 11s? Explain.

C7. Is the velocity of the car ever negative? Explain.

C8. Describe the features of (a) the strobe diagram, (b) your position vs. time graph, and (c) your velocity vs. time graph, that tell you that the car is slowing down.

50

Activity 12
Relating Strobe Diagrams to Plots of Position vs. Time and Velocity vs. Time

Reflection

R1. How would you recognize <u>accelerated</u> motion using a strobe diagram?

R2. If the speed of an object is constant, can its velocity ever be changing? If not, explain why not. If so, give one example of a situation in which the speed is constant but the velocity is changing.

R3. In each situation, you were asked to estimate either the position or the time at which something occurred (questions A1, A5, B4, C6).

    (a) For which situation was the estimate the easiest? Explain why.

    (b) For which was the estimate the most difficult? Explain why.

R4. For each of the estimates of either the position or time (questions A1, A5, B4, C6)...

    (a) ... which representation did you use, the strobe diagram, the position vs. time graph, or the velocity vs. time graph?

    (b) ... is it possible to use more than one representation to make your estimate? Explain.

Finding and Comparing Velocities

Purpose and Expected Outcome

In this activity you will use the definition of average velocity to determine and compare the average velocities of objects in a variety of situations. After you complete this activity you will know how to interpret the motion represented in graphs. You will also know how to compute average velocity.

Prior Experience / Knowledge Needed

You should know the definition of average velocity and be able to use it to calculate values of the average velocity.

Explanation of Activity

The positions of three objects have been measured at one-second time intervals. Below, we have plotted these data and connected them with dashed lines. In this activity, you will use these data to calculate the average velocity for different time intervals and use these calculations to analyze the motion of the objects.

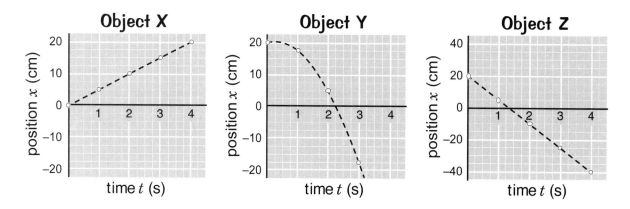

A1. Using the plots above, make a table showing the positions of objects X, Y, and Z.

TABLE OF POSITIONS

time	Position of Object X	Position of Object Y	Position of Object Z
(a) $t = 0$s			20cm
(b) $t = 1$s		17½cm	
(c) $t = 2$s	10cm		
(d) $t = 3$s			
(e) $t = 4$s		(not available)	

continued

A2. Using your table of positions, calculate the average velocities of the three objects during each one-second time intervals (0s to 1s, 1s to 2s, etc.) and make a table of average velocities, as shown below. (Some average velocities have been calculated already.)

TABLE OF AVERAGE VELOCITIES

time interval	Average Velocity of Object X	Average Velocity of Object Y	Average Velocity of Object Z
(a) 0s to 1s	5cm/s		
(b) 1s to 2s		$-12\frac{1}{2}$cm/s	
(c) 2s to 3s			–15cm/s
(d) 3s to 4s		(not available)	

A3. Compare the graphs of position vs. time with your calculations of average velocity. How can you determine with just a glance at the position vs. time graph of an object if it had a constant average velocity?

A4. How can you tell with just a glance at the position vs. time graph if an object is accelerating?

A5. Approximately where is object Y at t = 4s? Explain how you made this estimate.

A6. Estimate where objects X and Z are at t = 5s. Explain. What assumptions have you made?

Reflection

R1. Recall that the three plots of position vs. time were created using data taken at one-second time-intervals. Consider the motion of object X. How many different paths through the data are possible? Is the motion of object X <u>necessarily</u> uniform, as suggested by the data? What additional information is needed to conclude that the motion was, in fact, uniform?

R2. For what kind of position vs. time graph is the average velocity independent of the location or size of the time interval used to calculate the average velocity?

R3. How can you tell if an object is moving in the "negative" direction?

R4. If an object has a "positive" position, is the velocity positive or negative? Explain.

R5. If an object is moving in the "negative" direction...
  (a) ... what can you say about its position?
  (b) ... what can you say about its velocity?

14

Relating Graphs of Position vs. Time and Velocity vs. Time

Purpose and Expected Outcome

The purpose of this activity is to help you understand the relationship between graphical descriptions of position vs. time and velocity vs. time. After completing it you should be able to discuss the velocity of an object by looking at its position vs. time graph, or discuss its position by looking at its velocity vs. time graph.

Prior Experience / Knowledge Needed

By now, you should be very familiar with graphs of position and velocity vs. time! You also need to know the definition of displacement.

Explanation of Activity

Until now, you have studied both position vs. time graphs and velocity vs. time graphs, but usually they were examined separately. In this activity, you will consider both position vs. time graphs and velocity vs. time graphs <u>simultaneously</u>.

PART A: Interpreting Position and Velocity Graphs

Below is a set of position vs. time graphs, labeled A through E, for five different objects. Also, there is a set of velocity vs. time graphs, labeled F through J, for five different objects. The labels t_1 through t_5 indicate specific times. Use these graphs to answer all of Part A, and explain your reasoning for each answer.

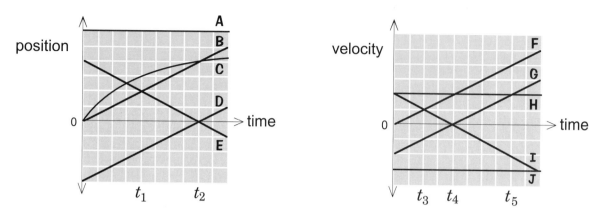

A1. Of objects A through E, which two have the same velocity at time t_2?

A2. Of objects F through J, which is farthest from the origin at time t_4?

A3. Of objects A through E, which has the largest speed at time t_2?

A4. Which objects have a negative overall displacement during the time interval shown?

A5. Of objects A through E, which has the smallest speed at time t_1?

A6. Which of the five velocity graphs could describe the same object as described by position graph E?

A7. Assuming object G starts at the origin, at what time is it farthest from the origin, t_3, t_4, or t_5? Explain.

A8. Which of the position graphs could describe the same object as velocity graph H?

A9. Which object A through E has the largest speed at $t = 0s$?

A10. Which objects A through E reverse direction?

A11. Which objects F through J reverse direction?

A12. Which object F through J has the largest displacement between $t = 0s$ and $t = t_5$?

58

Activity 14
Relating Graphs of Position vs. Time and Velocity vs. Time

PART B: The Effect of Situation Changes on Position and Velocity Graphs

Consider a marble sitting on a level track. At time $t = 2s$, the marble is bumped so that it rolls to the right with velocity +0.5m/s. (We have chosen our origin to be at the initial position of the marble, and the positive direction to be to the right.) The following graphs represent this motion:

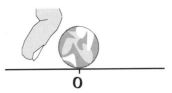

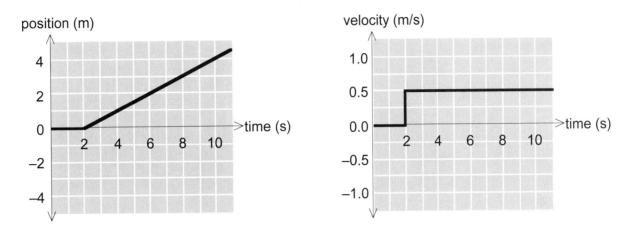

Refer to this situation and these graphs when completing questions B1–B5. In each case, draw the original graphs along with graphs that correspond to the description of each new situation.

B1. Assume now that the marble is given the same bump as before, but at $t = 4s$ instead of $t = 2s$. Draw a position vs. time graph and a velocity vs. time graph for this situation.

B2. This time, the marble is given an identical bump at $t = 2s$, but the bump is now to the left (in the negative direction) instead of to the right. Draw a position vs. time graph and a velocity vs. time graph for this situation.

B3. Now suppose that the marble is bumped exactly as the original, but this time the marble is located at $x = -2m$ when the bump occurs (at $t = 2s$). Draw the two graphs for this situation.

B4. This time, suppose that the marble is bumped to the right twice as hard as the original (so that it travels at 1m/s instead). Draw the graphs for this situation.

B5. Finally, suppose that everything is the same as the original **except** that there is a wall located at $x = 2m$ so that the marble suddenly reverses direction. (You may assume that the speed of the marble is the same before and after hitting the wall.) Draw the position vs. time and the velocity vs. time graphs for this case.

Reflection

R1. If an object is moving away from the origin, is the velocity necessarily positive? Explain.

R2. (a) If an object is moving in the positive direction, is its position necessarily positive also? Explain.

(b) What about its displacement? Is its displacement necessarily positive also? Explain.

60

Activity 14
Relating Graphs of Position vs. Time and Velocity vs. Time

More Relating Graphs of Position vs. Time and Velocity vs. Time

Purpose and Expected Outcome

The purpose of this activity is to help you understand the relationship between graphical descriptions of position and velocity. After completing it you should be able to use a position vs. time graph to describe the velocity of a moving object and to draw its velocity graph, and to use a velocity vs. time graph to describe the displacement of a moving object and (given its initial position) to draw its position graph.

Prior Experience / Knowledge Needed

You should have experience with position vs. time and velocity vs. time graphs.

Explanation of Activity

In this activity, you are presented with two complex situations involving a model train. Each situation allows you to study a different relationship between position and velocity. In the first situation, you are given a position vs. time graph for the train and from it, you will generate its velocity vs. time graph. In the second part, you will do the reverse.

PART A: Reading Velocity Information Contained in a Position vs. Time Graph

The following position vs. time graph describes the motion of a model train along a straight section of track during a certain 36-s time interval. The origin, $x = 0$, is chosen to be at the middle of the track section. The time interval has been divided into 7 segments (I through VII) with the times indicated. Use this graph to complete all of Part A.

Position vs. Time for a Model Train

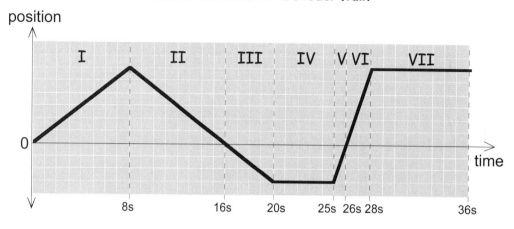

A1. Make a table to describe the motion of the model train between $t = 0$s and $t = 36$s.

(a) In row 1, indicate whether the train's position is positive, negative, or zero for each of the time-intervals (I through VII).

(b) In row 2, indicate whether the train's direction of motion is positive, negative, or zero.

(c) In row 3, indicate the size of the train's speed relative to the initial speed. That is, is the speed larger, smaller, or the same as its initial speed? (Some answers have been given.)

TABLE DESCRIBING THE MOTION OF THE MODEL TRAIN

	I	II	III	IV	V	VI	VII
POSITION (+, 0, or –)			0, then –				
DIRECTION OF MOTION (+, 0, or –)							
SPEED (relative to initial speed)	same!				larger		

A2. Draw a velocity vs. time graph for the train. You do not have enough information to label your axes with numbers, but try to keep everything approximately to scale.

PART B: Reading Position Information Contained in a Velocity Graph.

The following velocity vs. time graph describes the motion of a model train along a straight section of track. Assume the train starts at the origin $x = 0$m at time $t = 0$s. As in part A, the labels 10s through 120s indicate times for which the motion of the train changes.

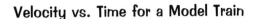

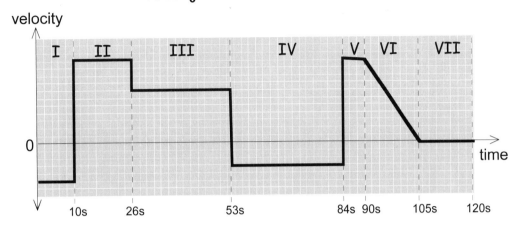

Velocity vs. Time for a Model Train

B1. Make a table to describe the motion of the model train.

(a) In row 1, indicate whether the train's direction of motion is positive, negative, or zero.

(b) In row 2, indicate whether the train's speed is larger, smaller, or the same as its initial speed.

(c) In row 3, indicate whether the train's displacement is positive, negative, or zero. (As before, some answers have been provided.)

TABLE DESCRIBING THE MOTION OF THE MODEL TRAIN

	I	II	III	IV	V	VI	VII
DIRECTION OF MOTION (+, 0, or –)		+					
SPEED (relative to initial speed)	same!		larger				
DISPLACEMENT (+, 0, or –)					–		

B2. Use your table to sketch the position of the train vs. time.

Reflection

R1. How would your graph of velocity vs. time in part A have changed if the origin of the coordinate system had been chosen differently?

R2. How would your graph of position vs. time in part B have changed if the origin was chosen differently? For instance, what if the initial position of the model train was $x = 1\text{m}$, what would the position vs. time graph have looked like?

R3. In both parts, the graphs of velocity vs. time change instantaneously at different times (e.g., at time $t = 10\text{s}$ in part B). Do you think this is possible in real-life? Explain.

R4. Can an object's position change instantaneously? Explain. What would have to be the speed of an object whose position changed instantaneously?

64

Activity 15
More Relating Graphs of Position vs. Time and Velocity vs. Time

Solving Constant-Velocity Problems Using Different Methods

Purpose and Expected Outcome

In this activity, you will analyze a situation and answer questions about it using three different representations of motion: a strobe diagram, algebraic equations, and position vs. time graphs. After completing the activity you should understand that there is usually more than one way to solve a problem, and that some ways are easier than others.

Prior Experience / Knowledge Needed

You should know and understand the following: how to draw and interpret strobe diagrams, how to apply kinematic equations to constant-velocity situations, and how to draw and interpret position vs. time graphs.

Explanation of Activity

Consider the following situation: Merinda and her little brother Joey are having a foot race from the edge of a road to a street lamp and back. At $t = 0$ seconds, Merinda starts; she runs at 2.5m/s all the way to the street lamp and back to the starting point. Joey is not yet ready at $t = 0$s, and doesn't start running until $t = 2$s; then he runs at 1.5m/s to the street lamp and back. (A drawing is provided below.)

METHOD A: Using Strobe Diagrams to Analyze Motion

A1. Make a strobe diagram by drawing symbols to show the positions of Merinda and Joey every second. We have drawn the first few symbols for you. Then use your strobe diagram to answer question A2.

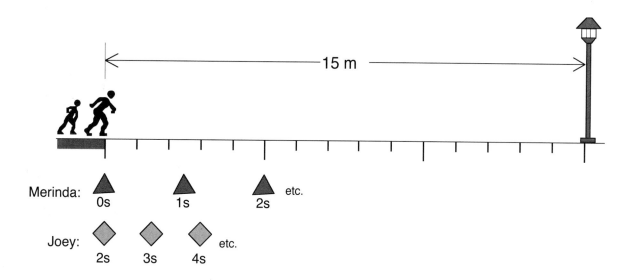

A2. While Joey is still running towards the street lamp, Merinda will pass him on her way back to the sidewalk.

(a) How far from the street lamp will this happen?

(b) At what time will this happen?

(c) What is their position relative to their starting point when this happens?

METHOD B: Using Algebra To Analyze Motion

Using <u>only</u> kinematic equations and algebra, answer the following questions about Merinda and Joey.

B1. (a) Find the position of Merinda and Joey when they pass each other.

    (b) When does this occur?

    (c) Do your answers agree with your results using method A?

B2. Where is Joey when Merinda reaches the street lamp?

METHOD C: Using Graphs to Analyze Motion

C1. Draw two position vs. time graphs, one for Merinda and one for Joey, from the time Merinda starts toward the street lamp until Joey returns to the sidewalk.

C2. (a) What is their position when they pass each other?

    (b) When does this occur?

    (c) Do your answers agree with your results using methods A and B?

C3. Where is Joey when Merinda reaches the street lamp? Does your answer agree with your result using method B?

C4. Where is Merinda when Joey reaches the street lamp?

C5. How far apart are Joey and Merinda when Merinda gets back to the starting point?

Reflection

R1. Of the three methods used in this activity...
   (a) ... which is easiest to work with?
   (b) ... which contains the most information?
   (c) ... which would you use to show someone else how to do these problems?
   (d) ... which would you like to learn better how to use?
   (e) ... which would you recommend others use to answer these types of questions?

R2. Does the expression "constant velocity" as used in this situation mean that all velocities are the same? If not, how many different velocities were used, and what were they? What does the expression "constant velocity" mean in this context?

A Final Note

We now have three methods for solving constant-velocity problems. In <u>this</u> context, using algebra was not the easiest. However, in some cases, you may still prefer to use algebra. The message is that you should <u>choose</u> your method before attempting to solve a problem. As you solve more problems, and think about how to solve them, choosing the easiest method will become more intuitive. Practice helps, and in the long run, this will save you time and frustration!

Solving Constant-Velocity Problems

Purpose and Expected Outcome

The purpose of this activity is to develop your ability to choose the best method to analyze and solve a constant-velocity kinematics problem. You have had some experience using strobe diagrams, graphs, and algebraic equation manipulation to solve such problems; now you should practice choosing which method to use when you have a problem you want to solve.

Prior Experience / Knowledge Needed

You will use nearly everything you have learned this year to solve these problems! Especially important are the three representations of motion (strobes, graphs, and algebra). Within the algebraic representation, you need to know that for constant-velocity motion in a straight line, the relationship between displacement, velocity, and time is: $\Delta x = v_x \, \Delta t$. Within the graphical representation, you need to know that the slope of x vs. t is the velocity, and the area "beneath" the v_x vs. t curve is the displacement.

Explanation of Activity

Each problem presents you with a situation and one or more questions about that situation. Use the method of your choice — strobe diagrams, manipulation of algebraic equations, or graphs — to answer the questions. **Be warned:** Some questions are much simpler by one method than by others. If you find you are having trouble with a problem, try a different method.

A1. Three bicyclists start a 20-km race at 12:00 noon. Bicyclist A travels at an average speed of 30km/h, B at 25km/h, and C at 22km/h.

(a) At what time does A finish the race?

(b) How far have B and C gone when A crosses the finish line?

A2. Two lacrosse players run towards each other from either end of a 120-yard lacrosse field. One runs at a constant velocity of 10 yards per second; the other at 7 yards per second. If they both start running at the same time...

(a) ...how much time passes before they meet?

(b) ...where on the field do they meet?

A3. Two football players, A and B, run towards each other from either end of a 100-yard football field. A runs at a constant velocity of 8 yards per second; B at 6 yards per second. A third player, C, starts at the same time as the other two, but from the 20-yard line, at the same end as A.

(a) If they all arrive at one place on the field at the same time, how fast is the third player running?

(b) Where on the field do they all meet?

A4. An astronaut pushes off from a space station, drifting away at 1.17m/s, while the station moves at 0.08m/s. The astronaut is connected to the station by a cable. 49 seconds later, the cable is pulled taut and stops the astronaut. How long is the cable?

continued

A5. A radio-controlled airplane flies north at 20km/h. The person holding the remote control is in a car driving west at 30km/h. If both start at the same time from the same point, and if the range of the remote controller is 10km, how far does the plane go before it is out of range of the controller?

A6. Train A leaves South Station at 5:00 PM, heading north at 60km/h towards Government Station. Train B is scheduled to leave Government Station at 5:20 PM and head south towards South Station. The two stations are 25km apart, and there are no stops in between. Samantha leaves Government Station at 5:05 PM in her Porsche 911, driving south at 90km/h on a road alongside the railroad tracks. When she sees train A heading north, she realizes it is on the track that train B is supposed to take. She turns around and speeds back to Government Station to prevent Train B from leaving (so that the two trains do not crash into each other!).

(a) How fast does she have to drive northward to get to Government Station before Train B leaves?

(b) If she reaches the station just in time, how far away is Train A when she gets there?

Reflection

R1. Of the six problems in this activity, how many did you solve using graphs? How many using algebra? And how many using strobe diagrams? Did any require a mix of methods? Which combinations were most useful?

R2. How many times did you make a sketch of the positions of the objects in the problems? If you did not do this at all, why not? Do you think it might have made any of the questions easier?

Recognizing Accelerated Motion

Purpose and Expected Outcome

This activity will help you to distinguish between situations in which an object is accelerating and those in which it is not. By looking at the speed and direction of motion separately, we can determine easily whether or not something is accelerating.

Prior Experience / Knowledge Needed

You need to know that the velocity has both a magnitude (which is usually referred to as the *speed*) and a direction (usually called the *direction of motion*). Acceleration occurs whenever the velocity changes.

Explanation of Activity and Example

For each object described below, state whether or not the object is accelerating and explain your answer.

> **Example.** A ball rolls down a steep hill.
>
> *Answer: Yes; the ball is accelerating because it speeds up as it rolls down the hill. (Its direction of motion might also be changing, but we don't have enough information to know for sure.)*

A1. A ball is attached to a string and swung in a horizontal circle.

A2. A baseball is thrown straight up into the air.

A3. A bullet is fired horizontally into a block of wood.

A4. A football is kicked off.

A5. A race car speeds around a track at constant speed.

A6. A truck drives down a straight highway at 55 mph.

A7. A bicyclist slows down to stop at a crosswalk.

Reflection

R1. The term *acceleration* is often used in our everyday language, and now you have seen how the same term is used in physics. Under what conditions is the meaning of the term the same in physics as it is in everyday use? Under what conditions is the meaning different? Explain.

R2. Consider a ball being thrown straight up into the air. As it travels up, the speed is getting smaller and smaller until it stops at the top. Therefore, on its way up, the ball is accelerating. The ball then starts to fall, traveling faster and faster until it hits something. On its way down, it is also accelerating. At the top, the ball is at rest. Imagine the instant just before it reaches the top and the instant just afterwards. Does the velocity change during that time interval? What must be true about the acceleration of the ball at its topmost point (when the ball is at rest)? Explain.

Describing Changes in Velocity

Purpose and Expected Outcome

The average acceleration over a given time interval is the change in velocity divided by the change in time. To describe acceleration properly requires that one correctly describe changes in velocity. In this activity you will analyze the changes in velocity for two situations. After completing this activity you should be able to determine the direction of acceleration for any type of motion.

Prior Experience / Knowledge Needed

You should be able to recognize when an object is accelerating. You should also understand how directed line segments can be used to describe velocity and changes in velocity.

Explanation of Activity

In part A, you will examine the motion of a toy car traveling in a straight line, then in part B, you will analyze the motion of a ball thrown in a curved arc.

PART A: Finding Changes in Velocity for Straight-Line Motion

Below, the motion of a toy car is represented by two strobe diagrams. The first strobe diagram shows the toy car moving toward the right (which we will take to be toward increasing values of the position). When the car reaches the final position shown it is picked up, rewound, and released facing the opposite direction. The second strobe diagram shows the car moving back toward its initial position. The velocity at each time is represented on the diagram by a directed line segment.

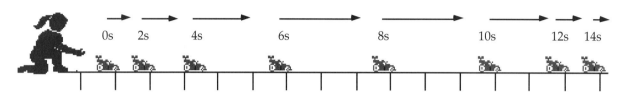

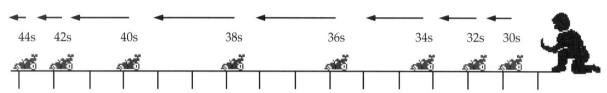

For each of the time intervals identified below, make a table showing (a) whether the change in velocity is zero or non-zero, (b) if the change in velocity is not zero draw a directed line segment representing the change in velocity, and (c) whether the acceleration is positive, negative, or zero. (Some of the answers have been provided.)

As the car moves to the right...

	time interval	(a) change in the car's velocity (zero or non-zero)	(b) directed line segment for the car's change in velocity	(c) direction of the car's average acceleration (+, 0, or −)
A1.	$t = 2$s to $t = 4$s			+ (to the right)
A2.	$t = 0$s to $t = 8$s		(1.5cm long)	
A3.	$t = 6$s to $t = 12$s	non-zero		
A4.	$t = 0$s to $t = 12$s			

continued

As the car moves to the left...

time interval	(a) change in the car's velocity (zero or non-zero)	(b) directed line segment for the car's change in velocity	(c) direction of the car's average acceleration (+, 0, or −)
A5. $t = 32$s to $t = 34$s	non-zero		
A6. $t = 30$s to $t = 38$s		← (1.5cm long)	
A7. $t = 40$s to $t = 42$s			+ (to the right)
A8. $t = 0$s to $t = 42$s			

Reflection (for Part A only)

R1. A marble is rolled at constant velocity toward a wall. The marble hits the wall and returns along its original path with the same speed as before. Is there any time interval for which the marble experiences an acceleration? If so, when? Explain.

R2. For motion along a straight line, under what conditions is the acceleration of an object positive (that is, points toward increasing values of position)?

R3. For motion along a straight line, under what conditions is the acceleration of an object negative (that is, points toward decreasing values of position)?

R4. For motion along a straight line, under what conditions is the acceleration of an object zero?

R5. Can an object have a non-zero acceleration even though its speed does not change? Explain.

PART B: Finding Changes in Velocity for Two-Dimensional Motion

The previous situation involved motion along a straight line. There are many situations where objects do not travel in straight lines. Below is a strobe diagram of a thrown ball moving in two dimensions.

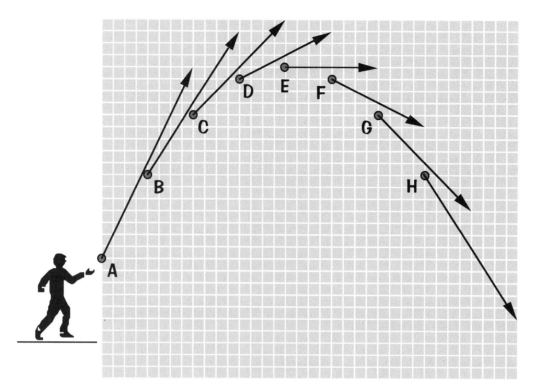

The velocity at each instant is represented as a directed line segment. For each of the time intervals identified below, make a table showing (a) whether the change in velocity is zero or non-zero, and (b) if the change in velocity is non-zero draw a directed line segment that you believe best represents the change in velocity.

B1. A to B

B2. D to E

B3. F to G

B4. D to F

B5. F to H

B6. <u>Where</u> do you think the ball would be located one time interval after H? Explain how you made your estimate.

Reflection (For Part B only)

R6. Consider the ball's *x*-coordinate (coordinate along the horizontal axis)? Is the rate of change of the ball's *x*-coordinate constant? Explain.

R7. Consider the ball's *y*-coordinate (coordinate along the vertical axis)? Is the rate of change of the ball's *y*-coordinate constant? Explain.

R8. Consider the directed line segments you drew to represent changes in velocity. What direction do they point? Are they all in the same direction?

R9. Is your answer to question R8 consistent with your answers to R6 and R7? Explain.

Recognizing Graphs of Acceleration vs. Time

Purpose and Expected Outcome

In this activity you will use graphs of acceleration vs. time to describe the physical motion of objects. To do this, we consider objects moving in a straight line and plot the (one-dimensional) acceleration versus time. After doing this activity you will know how to interpret acceleration vs. time graphs.

Prior Experience / Knowledge Needed

You should know how to use graphs of velocity vs. time to describe the motion of objects. You should understand the definition of acceleration as the change in velocity divided by the change in time.

Explanation of Activity and Examples

In this activity you are asked to recognize and associate graphs of acceleration vs. time with the physical motion of objects.

For each of the physical situations described below, identify which of the graphs of acceleration vs. time could represent the motion of the object in each physical situation described. Explain your reasoning. If necessary, specify which direction is positive.

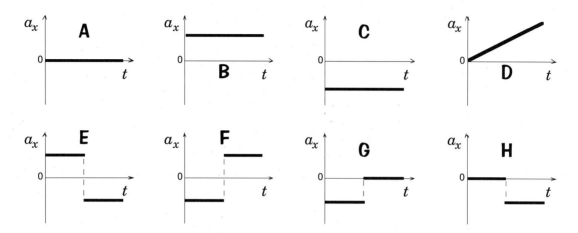

E1. A marble is rolling along a horizontal surface at constant speed away from the origin.

Answer: Graph A. The marble would have a constant velocity, because its speed is constant and its direction does not change. If the velocity is constant, then the acceleration is zero. The direction chosen to be positive does not matter.

E2. Starting from rest, a car speeds up until it reaches a speed of 60mph, and then cruises at 60mph.

Answer: Graph G. The acceleration is non-zero as the car speeds up, and then zero when it is traveling at constant speed. Graph G is the only possibility. The positive direction must be chosen to be opposite the direction of motion because the acceleration is negative. We have assumed that the acceleration is constant while the car is speeding up.

A1. A marble is released from the top of an inclined plane. Assume that positive x is measured down the plane.

continued

82

Activity 20
Recognizing Graphs of Acceleration vs. Time

A2. A block is released from rest on a smooth (frictionless) inclined plane. After traveling down the plane and reaching speed v, the block encounters a portion of the plane that is not smooth. The block moves onto the rough portion and stops after a distance d.

A3. A marble rolls along a horizontal surface at constant speed. After a while the marble passes onto a piece of felt and eventually rolls to a stop.

A4. A ball rolls with an initial velocity up an inclined plane. The ball comes to rest and then travels back down the plane.

A5. A ball is thrown straight up into the air. Take the origin to be at the level of the floor.

A6. A car is slowing down to stop for a red light. Before reaching the intersection, the light turns green, so the car speeds up again. Consider the time interval from the instant the car starts to slow down until it reaches a cruising speed.

Reflection

R1. Sometimes it is easier to first represent the motion of an object with a velocity vs. time graph and then use the velocity vs. time graph to figure out the acceleration vs. time graph. If you could not match one of the situations to a graph, or were unsure about your answer, go back and redo the problem, first drawing a velocity vs. time graph. Which of the situations have you redone in this way? Comment.

R2. If an object is speeding up, can its acceleration be negative? Explain. If an object is slowing down, can its acceleration be positive? Explain.

R3. If an object reverses its direction must the acceleration also change sign (that is, go from positive to negative or from negative to positive)? Explain.

Generating Sketches of Acceleration vs. Time

Purpose and Expected Outcome

In this activity, you will learn to make your own sketches of acceleration vs. time for objects moving in one dimension.

Prior Experience / Knowledge Needed

You should be familiar with acceleration vs. time graphs for motion in a straight line.

Explanation of Activity

Sketch the acceleration vs. time graph for the motion described during the specified interval of time in each situation. For each sketch, label the critical points with short descriptions of what is happening at those times.

Suggestion: Plot the velocity vs. time, then use it to sketch the acceleration vs. time.

A1. A box is pushed along the floor. At $t = 0$s the box is released. Assume that the box is being pushed in the positive direction. Sketch the acceleration of the box from the time of release until <u>after</u> it comes to rest.

A2. A man is driving along a straight highway with a constant speed of 50mph. In order to pass a truck, the man accelerates smoothly and quickly until his speed is 60mph, then gradually slows down to 50mph again. Sketch the acceleration of the car from just before the time the man begins to accelerate until just after he returns to a speed of 50mph.

continued

A3. A woman gets into an elevator which is waiting on the first floor of a building. She rides up to the fifth floor and gets out. Sketch the acceleration of the elevator from the time that the woman enters the elevator until she leaves.

A4. A toy car is released from rest at the top of an incline as shown to the right. The car hits a spring, reverses direction and travels back up the incline. Plot the acceleration of the toy car from the instant it is released until it comes to rest (momentarily) at the top of the incline. On a drawing of this situation, indicate the direction you have chosen to be positive.

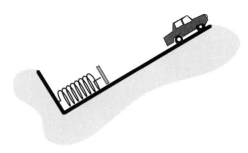

A5. A mass, M, hangs from a vertical spring as shown. The mass is pulled down until the spring is extended 10cm and then released at $t = 0$s. Plot the acceleration of the mass from $t = 0$s until it returns to the point of release. On a drawing of this situation, indicate the origin and the direction of increasing x.

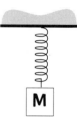

Reflection

R1. What does it mean when the acceleration changes from positive to negative or from negative to positive?

R2. Give at least one example of a situation in which the acceleration of an object changes direction <u>without</u> the direction of motion changing. Explain.

R3. Give at least one example of a situation in which the <u>direction of motion</u> changes without the direction of the acceleration changing. Explain.

R4. Give at least one example of a situation in which the position of an object is positive, its velocity is negative, and its acceleration is positive. Explain, preferably using diagrams.

86

Activity 21
Generating Sketches of Acceleration vs. Time

Translating Graphs of Acceleration vs. Time

Purpose and Expected Outcome

After doing this activity, you should be able to associate the motion of objects with graphs of acceleration vs. time.

Prior Experience / Knowledge Needed

You should be familiar with acceleration vs. time plots and understand the meaning of positive and negative acceleration.

Explanation of Activity

Using common classroom items (e.g. rubber or steel balls, springs, ramps, dynamics carts, etc.), make some object move in a manner that is qualitatively in accord with the following acceleration vs. time graphs. Write an explanation of how you accomplished this, noting the location of your origin and the orientation of your axis. Your explanations should be similar to the descriptions found in Activity 21.

A1. (a) What object did you make move like this graph?

(b) Describe how you did this.

(c) What does the first horizontal segment indicate about the motion of your object? What happens to the motion of your object when the acceleration changes from positive to negative? What happens during segment II?

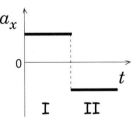

continued

© 1999 Kendall/Hunt Publishing Company

A2. (a) What object did you choose for this graph?

(b) Describe how you made the object move like the graph.

(c) What is the initial velocity of your object? What is happening to your object during segments I, II, and III?

(d) If your initial velocity was zero, repeat using a non-zero initial velocity.

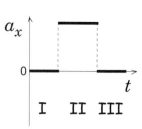

A3. (a) What object did you choose for this graph?

(b) Describe how you made the object move like the graph.

(c) What is the initial velocity of your object?

(d) Repeat using an initial velocity that is negative and a final velocity that is zero.

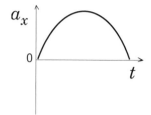

A4. (a) What object did you choose in this case?

(b) Describe how you made the object move like the graph.

(c) Indicate on a copy of this graph the instants of time at which your object is at rest.

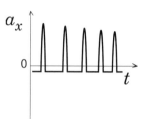

Reflection

R1. In this activity did all your objects start from rest? Could you have given each object an initial velocity and still satisfy the acceleration vs. time graph?

R2. Can you think of a situation in which the acceleration vs. time graph would change if the initial velocity of the object is changed? Give at least one example.

R3. Give an example of a situation in which an object has zero acceleration and zero velocity.

R4. Can an object have a non-zero acceleration at the same time that its velocity is zero? Explain and give at least one example.

88

Activity 22
Translating Graphs of Acceleration vs. Time

Calculating Average Acceleration

Purpose and Expected Outcome

In this activity you will use the definition of average acceleration to determine and compare the average acceleration of objects in a variety of situations. After you complete this activity you will know how to compute average acceleration from a velocity vs. time graph.

Prior Experience / Knowledge Needed

You should know and understand the definition of average acceleration as the change in velocity divided by the change in time. You should also be familiar with velocity vs. time graphs.

Explanation of Activity

In this activity you will calculate the average acceleration from the velocity vs. time plots for four different objects and then make comparisons among them. The velocity vs. time graphs for all four objects, A, B, C and D, are shown below using the same set of axes for each object.

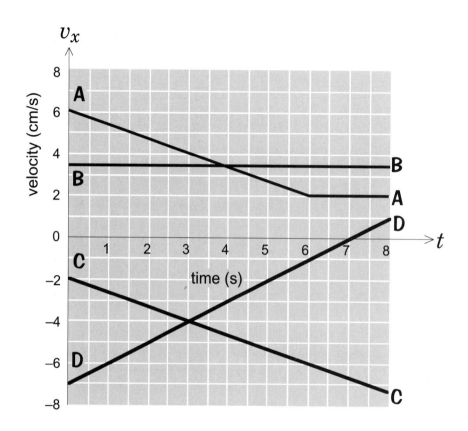

A1. What is the average acceleration over the interval 0 to 3 seconds for Object A?

A2. What is the average acceleration over the interval 2 to 4 seconds for Object A?

A3. What is the average acceleration over the interval 0 to 8 seconds for Object A?

A4. Is your answer to A1 the same as or different from the answer to A2? Explain.

A5. Is your answer to A1 the same as or different from the answer to A3? Explain.

continued

A6. What is the average acceleration over the interval 2 to 4 seconds for Object B?

A7. What is the average acceleration over the interval 4 to 6 seconds for Object C?

A8. Do any two objects ever have the same average acceleration? If so, which objects and for what time interval?

A9. Which object has the largest average acceleration over a very short time interval near $t = 3s$?

A10. Which object has the largest average acceleration over a very short time interval near $t = 7s$?

A11. What is the (instantaneous) acceleration of Object D at $t = 6$ seconds?

A12. Which objects have a smaller speed at $t = 6$ seconds than at $t = 0s$?

Reflection

R1. In question A12 you identified objects for which the speed was decreasing. What, if anything, can you say about the acceleration of an object when its speed is decreasing? Explain.

R2. For what kind of velocity vs. time graph is the average acceleration independent of the time interval used to calculate the average acceleration?

R3. From a velocity vs. time graph how can you tell at a glance if the object is speeding up? How can you tell if the object is slowing down?

R4. From a velocity vs. time graph how can you tell at a glance that the acceleration is positive? How can you tell that the acceleration is negative?

Relating Strobe Diagrams to Graphs of Acceleration vs. Time

Purpose and Expected Outcome

After completing this activity you will be able to construct a graph of acceleration vs. time from a strobe diagram. You will understand how various features of a strobe diagram are related to the features of the corresponding acceleration vs. time graph.

Prior Experience / Knowledge Needed

You should be able to interpret velocity and acceleration graphs. You need to be able to sketch an acceleration vs. time graph from a velocity vs. time graph. You should know how to sketch a velocity vs. time graph given a strobe diagram.

Explanation of Activity

Shown below are two situations. In each case you are shown a strobe diagram of the motion of an object. Use the strobe diagram to construct a sketch of the velocity vs. time graph and the acceleration vs. time graph. Answer all questions that follow each situation.

SITUATION A: Motion of a Wind-Up Toy

A girl winds up a toy car and places it on the floor. When she lets go of the car it moves as shown in the strobe picture. The car is shown at 2s intervals. **Note:** Use 2cm = 1m as the scale of the diagram.

A1. Sketch (a) the velocity vs. time graph and (b) the acceleration vs. time graph for the toy car. Make sure you label all the axes.

For each diagram of the motion of the toy car, describe the features that indicate (a) when the car is speeding up and (b) when the car is slowing down.

diagram	(a) The car is speeding up when...	(b) The car is slowing down when...
A2. Strobe diagram		
A3. Velocity vs. Time graph		
A4. Acceleration vs. Time graph		

A5. If at t = 0s the car were pointed in the opposite direction, how would your answers to questions A1, A2, A3, and A4 change?

A6. Can one tell if an object's speed is changing using <u>only</u> its acceleration vs. time graph? Explain.

A7. Can one tell if an object's speed is increasing or decreasing using <u>only</u> its acceleration vs. time graph? Explain.

94

Activity 24
Relating Strobe Diagrams to Graphs of Acceleration vs. Time

SITUATION B: Motion of a Small Rubber Ball

A small rubber ball rolls across the floor. For a period of time it passes over a piece of felt. After leaving the felt, it collides with a wall and rebounds, passing over the felt a second time. Assume that the motion of the ball is along a straight line path. The strobe diagram for the motion of the ball is shown below. Assume that the time interval between strobes is 0.5s.

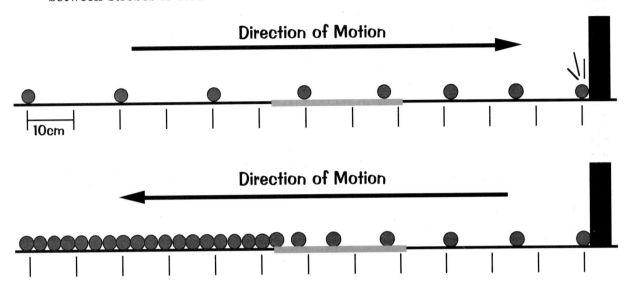

B1. Sketch (a) the velocity vs. time graph and (b) the acceleration vs. time graph for the rubber ball. Make sure you label all the axes.

For each diagram of the motion of the rubber ball, describe the features that indicate: (a) when the ball is slowing down, (b) when its direction of motion is negative, and (c) when its acceleration is negative.

diagram	(a) The ball is slowing down when...	(b) The ball's direction of motion is negative when...	(c) The ball's acceleration is negative when...
B2. Strobe diagram			
B3. Velocity vs. Time graph			
B4. Acceleration vs. Time graph			

Reflection

R1. In this activity did you always use your sketch of the velocity vs. time to help sketch the acceleration vs. time graph? Is it possible to sketch the acceleration vs. time graph directly from the strobe diagram?

R2. Is it easier for you to characterize the motion (for example, moving in a negative direction, negative acceleration, slowing down, etc.) using a strobe diagram, a velocity vs. time graph, or an acceleration vs. time graph? Explain.

R3. Is there more information in a strobe diagram or in an acceleration vs. time graph? Explain.

R4. What do you consider to be the main advantages of representing the motion of an object with graphs rather than strobe diagrams

96

Activity 24
Relating Strobe Diagrams to Graphs of Acceleration vs. Time

Relating Graphs and Kinematic Functions

Purpose and Expected Outcome

In this activity you will develop expressions for the kinematic quantities as functions of time using only velocity vs. time graphs for constant-acceleration motion. After completing this activity you will be able to use a velocity vs. time graph to write the velocity and position as functions of time.

Prior Experience / Knowledge Needed

You should understand why the area under the velocity vs. time graph is equal to an object's displacement and the slope of the velocity vs. time graph is equal to the object's acceleration.

You should be familiar with the general expression for a straight line ($y = mx + b$) and you should know how to determine specific values for the slope and intercept from a straight-line graph. You should also know how to find the area of simple planar objects, such as a rectangle and a triangle.

Explanation of Activity

In each of the problems below you are given a velocity vs. time graph, and asked to find values or expressions for other kinematic quantities.

PART A: Finding Displacement Using a Velocity Graph

A1. An object moves according to the velocity vs. time plot shown at the right.

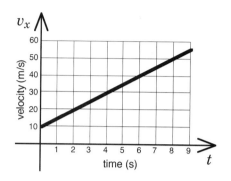

(a) What is the acceleration of the object? (What is the object's change in velocity every second?)

(b) What is the initial velocity of the object? (What is the velocity of the object at $t = 0s$?)

(c) Write a general expression for $v_x(t)$? (In other words, according to the plot at right, what is the velocity of the object at any particular time t?)

A2. Consider the modified plot at right. The area under the velocity plot between $t = 0s$ and $t = 2s$ can be found as the sum of the area below $v_x = 10m/s$ (shown as a shaded rectangle) and the area above $v_x = 10m/s$ (shown as a speckled triangle).

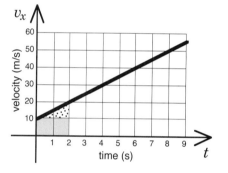

Using this procedure, make a table showing the areas under the velocity graph for the nine time intervals listed below. Note that all time-intervals start at $t = 0s$.

	time interval	Area below $v_x = 10m/s$ (rectangle)	Area above $v_x = 10m/s$ (triangle)	Total area under graph (rectangle + triangle)
(a)	0s to 1s			$12\frac{1}{2}m$
(b)	0s to 2s		10m	
(c)	0s to 3s	30m		
(d)	0s to 4s		40m	
(e)	0s to 5s			$112\frac{1}{2}m$
(f)	0s to 6s			
(g)	0s to 7s			
(h)	0s to 8s			
(i)	0s to 9s			

A3. Plot the total area under the velocity graph vs. the <u>endpoint</u> of the time interval.

This is the displacement of the object between time $t = 0s$ and time t.

PART B: Finding an Expression for Position Using a Velocity Graph

Consider the diagram of the velocity vs. time of an object shown below. An object has an initial velocity of v_0 and its velocity increases at a constant rate of a_1. Answer all questions in this problem using quantities that appear in the diagram.

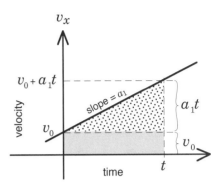

B1. Write an expression for the area of the shaded rectangle in terms of v_0 and t.

B2. Write an expression for the area of the speckled triangle area in terms of a_1 and t.

B3. Write a general expression for the total area under the velocity vs. time graph between 0 and t in terms of the initial velocity (v_0) and the constant acceleration (a_1).

This is the object's displacement between time t = 0s and time t.

B4. Assuming that the object starts at $x = x_0$ at $t = 0$s, write a general expression for $x(t)$, the position of the object at time t.

PART C: Finding an Expression for Position When the Acceleration is Negative

Consider the diagram of the velocity vs. time of an object shown below. The object starts out traveling with a velocity of v_0, and its velocity *decreases* at a constant rate of a_2. Answer all questions in this problem using quantities that appear in the diagram. Note that now the acceleration of the object is negative. (That is, $a_2 < 0$.)

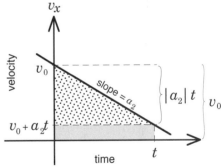

C1. Write an expression for the area of the shaded rectangle in terms of v_0, $\left|a_2\right|$, and t.

C2. Write an expression for the area of the speckled triangle area in terms of $\left|a_2\right|$ and t.

C3. Write a general expression for the total area under the velocity vs. time graph between 0 and t in terms of the initial velocity (v_0) and the constant acceleration (a_2). (Note that the acceleration is negative, so $a_2 = -\left|a_2\right|$.) Simplify your expression as much as possible.

This is the object's displacement between time t = 0s and time t.

C4. Assuming that the object starts at $x = x_0$ at $t = 0$s, write a general expression for $x(t)$, the position of the object at time t.

C5. Compare this expression with the expression you derived in question B4 of Part B. Are they the same or different?

A Note to Students

The general expression derived for the position x of an object at time t can be applied to any situation in which the acceleration is constant. The initial position x_0, the initial velocity v_0, and the constant acceleration (a_1 or a_2) can each be either positive, negative, or zero. The same expression works for all (nine!) possible combinations of initial conditions. To verify this result, simply repeat the derivation of part B or C using the combination you wish to check.

However, if the acceleration does not have the same value for the entire interval from time $t = 0s$ to time t, then this expression is no longer valid. In those cases for which the acceleration changes, simply use areas below the velocity vs. time graph to find the displacement of the object.

Integration of Ideas

Below are four different statements concerning the relationships between graphs of position, velocity, and acceleration vs. time. Complete each statement, making sure that each is completely different from those statements preceding it. (For items in square brackets, choose exactly one.)

I1. The [*slope of* / *area below*] the position vs. time graph at some time t is equal to the [*displacement* / *velocity* / *acceleration*] at the same time t.

I2. The [*slope of* / *area below*] the [*position* / *velocity*] vs. time graph between two times is equal to the change in [*position* / *velocity*] between the same two times.

I3. The [*slope of* / *area below*] the _____ vs. time graph _____ is equal to the change in [*position* / *displacement* / *velocity* / *acceleration*] [*between* / *at*] the same [*time t* / *two times*].

I4. The _____ the _____ vs. time graph _____ is equal to the [*position* / *velocity* / *acceleration*] _____ the same _____ .

Relating Kinematic Quantities with Kinematic Functions

Purpose and Expected Outcome

The purpose of this activity is to help you understand the relationship between kinematic quantities, such as position, displacement, velocity, and acceleration, and algebraic expressions for these quantities as functions of time.

Prior Experience / Knowledge Needed

You should be able to interpret position, velocity and acceleration vs. time graphs. Also, you need to know the relationships between graphs of position, velocity, and acceleration vs. time. (For example, the slope of position vs. time is the velocity.) You should be familiar with algebraic expressions for position, displacement, and velocity as functions of time.

Explanation of Activity and Example

There are two parts in this activity. In the first part, you will write the algebraic expressions of velocity, position or displacement based on information given about the situation. In the second part, you will determine the values of specific kinematic quantities given algebraic expressions for either the position or velocity.

In both parts, sketches of velocity vs. time and position vs. time should help you to answer the questions.

PART A: Writing Expressions for Position, Displacement and Velocity

For each of the situations below, use the given information to write the desired algebraic expression. You are encouraged to make sketches and plots to help you answer the questions.

Example. A car enters the freeway traveling at 50mph (about 22m/s) and speeds up to 65mph (about 29m/s) at a rate of 0.7m/s^2. Write expressions (a) for the velocity, and (b) for the displacement of the car. (c) For what time interval are these expressions valid?

Answer: If we assume that t = 0s occurs just as the car enters the freeway, then the initial velocity is 22m/s. The acceleration is 0.7m/s^2, so the velocity of the car is:

$$v_x = 22\text{m/s} + (0.7\text{m/s}^2)t$$

and its displacement is:

$$\Delta x = (22\text{m/s})t + (0.35\text{m/s}^2)t^2$$

These expressions are valid only until t = 10s, when the car reaches its cruising speed of 65mph.

A1. You are approaching a traffic light that has just turned green. At the intersection, a car which was stopped, begins to come toward you, speeding up at a rate of 2m/s^2.

    (a) What is the car's velocity as a function of time?

    (b) How far has the car traveled in time t?

    (c) What is the car's position as a function of time?

A2. A ball rolls up an incline and follows the velocity graph shown at right.

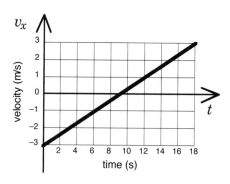

    (a) What is the initial velocity of the ball?

    (b) What is the acceleration of the ball? Is the acceleration constant? Explain.

    (c) Write an expression for the velocity of the ball at an arbitrary time t while on the incline.

    (d) Write an expression for the displacement of the ball between t = 0s and time t.

continued

A3. A marble is rolling along a hard surface at 3m/s when it rolls onto a piece of carpet, causing it to slow down at a rate of 0.6m/s^2.

   (a) Write an expression for the velocity of the marble from the instant it hits the carpet.

   (b) What is the displacement of the marble at time t after hitting the carpet?

   (c) For what time interval are your expressions valid? Explain.

A4. A cart has a position given by the expression, $x = -4\text{m} + (6\text{m/s})t - (2\text{m/s}^2)t^2$.

   (a) What direction is the cart moving initially? Explain why you think so.

   (b) When does the cart reach the origin (if ever)? Explain your answer.

   (c) Write an expression for the velocity of the cart as a function of time.

   (d) When does the cart stop and change directions? Explain your answer.

PART B: Extracting Kinematic Information from Algebraic Expressions

For each of the algebraic expressions below, determine, <u>if possible</u>, (a) the acceleration, (b) the initial velocity, (c) the velocity at $t = 10\text{s}$, and (d) the position at $t = 10\text{s}$. (Some values have been determined already.)

Algebraic Expression	(a) acceleration	(b) initial velocity	(c) velocity at $t = 10$s	(d) position at $t = 10$s
B1. $v_x = 1\text{m/s} + (2\text{m/s}^2)t$			21m/s	
B2. $x = 5\text{m} + (8\text{m/s})t + (4\text{m/s}^2)t^2$	8m/s^2			485m
B3. $x = (5\text{m/s})t - (2\text{m/s}^2)t^2$		5m/s	−35m/s	
B4. $v_x = -10\text{m/s} + (3\text{m/s}^2)t$	3m/s^2			
B5. $x = (2\text{m/s}^2)t^2 + (1\text{m/s})t - 15\text{m}$			41m/s	
B6. $v_x = 10\text{m/s}$		10m/s		
B7. $x = (1\text{m/s}^2)t^2$				
B8. $x = (2\text{m/s})t + 4\text{m}$				24m

Reflection

R1. While you were answering question A1...

    (a) ... what did you assume was the initial velocity of the car? Why is this choice justified?

    (b) ... where is the origin of your coordinate system located?

R2. To answer question A2, were you able to find a single expression for the velocity of the ball that covers the entire 18-second time interval? Explain why or why not.

R3. In question A3, where did you choose your origin? What is the initial position of the marble?

R4. Is it possible to determine the location of an object given only its velocity? Explain why or why not. If it is not possible, what additional information is needed to be able to determine its location?

R5. Give an example of a situation in which the initial position is negative, the initial velocity is positive, and the acceleration is negative. Draw the situation, showing where the origin is located and indicating the direction chosen to be positive.

27

Relating Graphs of Position, Velocity, and Acceleration vs. Time

Purpose and Expected Outcome

The purpose of this activity is to help you understand the relationship between graphical descriptions of acceleration vs. time and those of position and velocity vs. time. After completing the activity you should be able to describe the acceleration of an object given its position or velocity vs. time graph, as well as describe the velocity and position of an object given its acceleration vs. time graph.

Prior Experience / Knowledge Needed

You should be able to interpret position, velocity and acceleration vs. time graphs. Also, you need to know the relationships between graphs of position, velocity, and acceleration vs. time. (For example, the slope of position vs. time is the velocity.)

Explanation of Activity and Examples

Consider a marble sitting on a level surface. At time $t = 0$s the marble is given a push so that it rolls to the right with a constant velocity of +0.5m/s. The graphs shown below represent this motion. Refer to this situation and these graphs when completing situations A, B, and C. In each case, the situation will be changed. Re-draw the position, velocity, and acceleration vs. time graphs to match the changes made to the situation. Then use the graphs to answer questions about the motion of the marble.

Graphs of Position, Velocity, and Acceleration vs. Time for the Original Situation

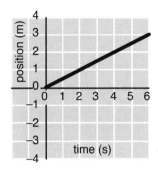 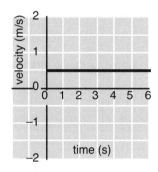 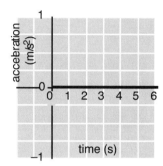

E1. What is the initial position of the marble?

Answer: *According to the position vs. time graph, the initial position is* $x = 0m$.

The original situation is now changed so that the marble is given an initial velocity of –0.5m/s. This is the only change made.

E2. Plot the position, velocity, and acceleration vs. time of the marble.

Answer:

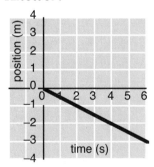 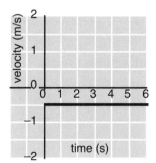 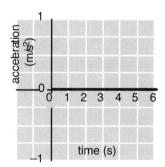

Explanation: *The marble now moves to the left with a constant speed of 0.5m/s. Everything else about the situation is the same as before: Motion starts at $t = 0$s at $x = 0m$.*

106

Activity 27
Relating Graphs of Position, Velocity, and Acceleration vs. Time

SITUATION A: Starting at a Negative Position

The original situation is changed so that the marble is given a push at position $x = -2$m at time $t = 1$s. These are the only changes made.

A1. Plot (a) the position, (b) the velocity, and (c) the acceleration of the marble vs. time.

A2. How is the position vs. time graph different from the original? How is it the same? Explain.

A3. What is the change in position of the marble between $t = 2$s and $t = 6$s? How does this value compare to the original change in position between the same two times? Explain.

A4. What is the change in position of the marble between $t = 0$s and $t = 4$s? How does this value compare to the original change in position between the same two times? Explain.

SITUATION B: Rolling onto a Large Piece of Felt

The original situation is changed so that the marble now rolls onto a large piece of felt at $t = 2$s. The felt causes the marble to slow down uniformly, eventually stopping at $t = 6$s.

B1. Plot (a) the position, (b) the velocity, and (c) the acceleration of the marble vs. time. (**Suggestion**: Draw the velocity vs. time graph first, then draw the other two.)

B2. Between $t = 2$s and $t = 6$s, is the position vs. time graph a straight line or a curve? Explain.

B3. Where does the marble come to rest? Explain.

B4. How far does the marble travel on the felt? Explain.

SITUATION C: Rolling onto a Small Piece of Felt

The original situation is changed in three ways: (1) the initial speed of the marble is 1m/s; (2) at $t = 2$s, the marble rolls onto a thin piece of felt causing the marble to slow down uniformly at a rate of 0.25m/s^2; and (3) at $t = 4$s, the marble rolls off the felt, continuing at constant velocity. A diagram is shown below.

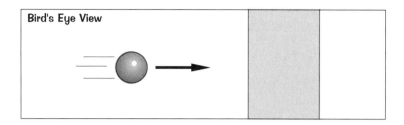

Bird's Eye View

C1. Plot (a) the position, (b) the velocity, and (c) the acceleration of the marble vs. time.

C2. What is the velocity of the marble (a) at $t = 3$s and (b) at $t = 5$s? Explain.

C3. How wide is the piece of felt? Explain.

Reflection

R1. Can merely changing the initial position of an object change the velocity vs. time or acceleration vs. time graphs for an object? Explain.

R2. How would you determine the velocity or position of an object using its acceleration vs. time graph?

R3. Which graphs were the most difficult for you to construct? What made it difficult to construct them?

R4. In your estimation, is it usually more difficult to use a position vs. time graph to help construct the velocity and acceleration vs. time graphs, or to use the acceleration vs. time graph to help construct the velocity and position vs. time graphs? Explain.

108

Activity 27
Relating Graphs of Position, Velocity, and Acceleration vs. Time

28

Comparing Graphs of Velocity vs. Time and Displacement vs. Time

Purpose and Expected Outcome

After completing this activity you will be able to describe the displacement vs. time graph given the velocity vs. time graph.

Prior Experience / Knowledge Needed

You should be able to imagine the motion of an object given a graph of the object's motion, and to sketch the graph of an object's motion from an image. You should know how the slope of the position (or displacement) vs. time graph relates to the velocity, and how the area below the velocity vs. time graph relates to the displacement. Finally, you should know that when the velocity is negative, the displacement is also negative, so areas below the time axis are negative.

Explanation of Activity

In this activity you are asked to identify and associate graphical sketches of curves with other sketches that represent the area under the curve. For each sketch of v_x vs. t on the following page, there is a sketch of Δx vs. t that corresponds to the area below the v_x vs. t curve. For each v_x vs. t sketch, determine the corresponding Δx vs. t curve. Assume that all curved portions of sketches are parabolic (that is, describable as a quadratic function).

Suggestion: For each velocity vs. time graph, use areas to determine what the displacement vs. time curve should look like. Then use the <u>slope</u> of your displacement curve to verify the velocity curve. Once your displacement curve is checked, choose the given displacement curve that most closely matches yours.

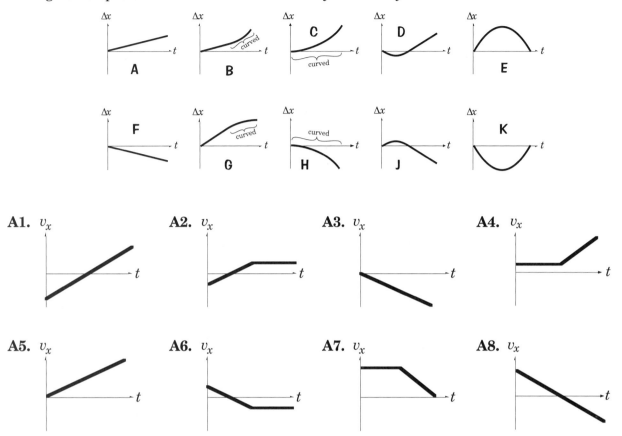

R1. How can you tell from the velocity vs. time graph when an object has come back to its initial position?

R2. How can you tell when the velocity of an object is zero from a position (or displacement) vs. time graph?

R3. If a portion of the position vs. time graph is a straight line segment what can you say about the velocity vs. time graph during the same time interval?

R4. Describe the main differences in the displacement vs. time graphs for the following two situations:
1. The velocity is negative and the speed is <u>decreasing</u> at a constant rate.
2. The velocity is negative and the speed is <u>increasing</u> at a constant rate.

Reflection

110

Activity 28
Comparing Graphs of Velocity vs. Time and Displacement vs. Time

Translating Between Different Representations of Accelerated Motion

Purpose and Expected Outcome

Motion can be described in many different ways. It can be described using words, graphs, strobe diagrams, or equations. Each of these different descriptions, or representations, has its own virtues and drawbacks. Being able to translate from one representation to another is a very useful skill. The purpose of this activity is to help you associate these various ways that motion can be described and learn how to translate among them.

Prior Experience / Knowledge Needed

You should be familiar with graphs of linear (straight line) and quadratic (parabolic) functions. You should also have some experience with expressions for position and velocity of an object undergoing constant acceleration. In particular, you should be very familiar with the proper use of the expressions, $x = x_0 + v_{0x}t + \frac{1}{2}a_x t^2$ and $v_x = v_{0x} + a_x t$.

Explanation of Activity and Example

There are three parts to this activity. In the first part, you will generate graphs to represent the motion of different objects in several situations. Sometimes the information needed to make the graphs will be in words, and sometimes the information will be given using equations. In the second part, you will generate equations to represent motion, and the given information will be either in words or in graphs. Finally, in the third part, you will generate both equations and graphs based on a variety of given information.

PART A: Generating Graphical Descriptions of Motion

In this part you are asked to generate plots of one or more of the kinematic quantities based upon information provided in verbal form.

Example. A marble is rolled with an initial velocity of 0.2m/s up an inclined plane. The marble is released part way up the incline at a point 0.25 meters from the bottom of the plane. While on the incline the marble has a constant acceleration of 0.1m/s² down the plane. Make a plot of the velocity of the marble vs. time from the time of release until 5 seconds later.

Answer: A plot of velocity vs. time for 5 seconds is shown below.

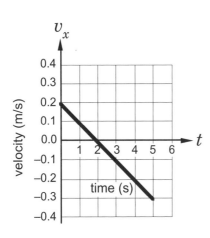

Explanation: First note that the acceleration is constant. The general expression for the velocity when the acceleration is constant is $v_x(t) = a_x t + v_{0x}$. *We will choose "up the plane" to be the positive direction. From the verbal description above we find:*

$$a_x = -0.1\text{m/s}^2$$

where the minus sign means that the direction of the acceleration is down the plane, and:

$$v_{0x} = 0.2\text{m/s}$$

which is positive since the marble is initially going up the plane. So, the function plotted on the left is:

$$v_x(t) = -0.1t + 0.2$$

A1. A car is traveling on a straight road with a constant speed of 25m/s. Plot the displacement of the car from its starting position as a function of time over the interval $t = 0$s to $t = 8$s.

A2. A boy throws a ball vertically into the air. The ball has an initial velocity of 15m/s and is released when it is 1 meter above the ground. Plot (a) the velocity and (b) the vertical height of the ball as functions of time from the instant of release until the ball hits the ground. Use as the acceleration of the ball the approximate value of –10m/s². (Label the axes carefully.)

(c) What is the maximum height of the ball above the ground?

(d) At what instant of time does the ball reach its maximum height?

(e) What is the speed of the ball when it reaches its maximum height?

continued

A3. At the start of a 100-meter race a woman sprinter accelerates with a constant acceleration of 2m/s^2 for the first 6 seconds and then finishes the race at constant speed.

    (a) Plot the velocity of the woman for the duration of the race.

    (b) How long does it take her to run 100 meters?

    (c) What is her maximum speed?

PART B: Generating Functional Descriptions of Motion

In this part you are asked to generate equations for kinematic quantities based upon information provided in verbal and/or graphical form.

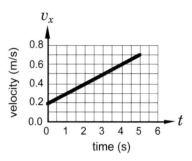

B1. An object has an initial position of 5 meters and has the velocity vs. time plot shown at right.

    (a) Obtain an expression for $v_x(t)$, the velocity as a function of time.

    (b) Obtain an expression for $x(t)$, the position as a function of time.

    (c) Where is the object at $t = 4\text{s}$?

B2. An object accelerates at a constant rate, starting from rest at the origin. After two seconds the object has a velocity of 6m/s in the positive direction.

    (a) What is the acceleration of the object?

    (b) Obtain an expression for $x(t)$.

    (c) Where is the object at $t = 10\text{s}$?

PART C: Generating Graphical and Functional Descriptions of Motion

In this part you are asked to generate both graphs and equations for different kinematic quantities based upon information provided in verbal form.

C1. At $t = 1\text{s}$, an object is 5 meters to the right of the origin. At $t = 2\text{s}$, the object has a velocity of 5m/s. At $t = 4\text{s}$, the object has a velocity of 9m/s. Assume constant acceleration throughout the motion of the object.

    (a) Plot the velocity vs. time from $t = 0\text{s}$ to $t = 8\text{s}$.

    (b) Obtain an expression for $v_x(t)$. (**Suggestion:** Use your graph to find the initial velocity and the acceleration.)

    (c) Obtain an expression for $x(t)$. (**Suggestion:** Use areas below your velocity graph to find the displacement between $t = 0\text{s}$ and $t = 1\text{s}$. Then work backwards from the given information above to find the position of the object at $t = 0\text{s}$.)

continued

C2. A block having an initial velocity of 1m/s has an acceleration that is given by the plot below.

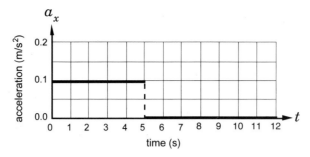

(a) Plot $v_x(t)$ from $t = 0$s until $t = 10$s.

(b) If the block starts at the origin, obtain an expression for the position as a function of time between $t = 0$s and $t = 5$s.

(c) Where is the object at $t = 5$s, 6s, 7s, 8s, 9s, and 10s?

(d) Plot the position vs. time from $t = 0$s to $t = 10$s.

(e) Find a valid expression for $x(t)$ between $t = 5$s and $t = 10$s.

Reflection

R1. How can you tell if an object is accelerating using only its position vs. time graph?

R2. How can you tell if an object is accelerating using only the algebraic expression for its position as a function of time?

R3. How can you tell if an object is accelerating using only the algebraic expression for its velocity as a function of time?

R4. The position of an object at time t is given by $x = 1$m $+ (2$m/s$)t + (3$m/s$^2)t^2$. What is the velocity of the object at time t? Explain.

R5. (a) Which kinematic quantities can **not** be determined from the expressions for $x(t)$?

(b) Which can not be determined from $v_x(t)$? Explain.

Graphical Representations of Motion: Reflection and Integration

Purpose and Expected Outcome

There are several kinematic quantities (position, displacement, velocity, acceleration, etc.) that we have represented graphically. We have spent considerable time interpreting and relating such graphs. Most of the time we have focused on one or two major issues. In this activity you must "put it all together" to answer a wide range of questions related to graphical representations of motion. After completing this activity you should feel comfortable analyzing graphical representations of motion, no matter what kinematic quantity, and no matter what situation. You should also have a good understanding of the relationships between the various kinematic quantities.

Prior Experience / Knowledge Needed

You should be thoroughly familiar with graphical representations of motion.

Explanation of Activity and Example

Below are shown a set of qualitative graphs of the motion of different objects in different situations, but <u>without</u> the vertical axis labeled. The kinematic variable to be associated with the graphs will be indicated in the questions below. In each case (a) indicate <u>all</u> of the sketches that satisfy the conditions specified in the question. (b) If more than one sketch meets the conditions specified in the question, indicate the feature that all of the selected sketches have in common. (c) If none of the graphs meets the conditions of the question, sketch a graph that does satisfy the conditions.

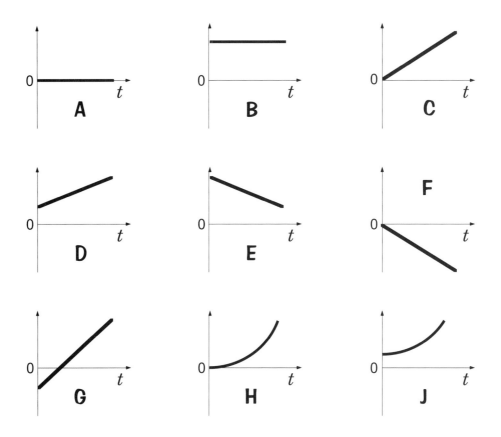

Example. If the vertical axis (ordinate) in each of the above sketches were the <u>velocity</u> of an object, which of the sketches could correspond to a situation in which the object has a constant non-zero positive acceleration?

Answer: The acceleration is the slope of the velocity vs. time graph. The only sketches having a constant, positive slope are C, D, and G. Note that sketches A and B are horizontal, which means that the slope is zero and the object has zero acceleration. Sketches E and F have negative slopes, and sketches H and J do not have a constant slope.

A1. If the vertical axis corresponds to the <u>position</u> of an object, which of the sketches would be appropriate for an object having constant, non-zero velocity?

A2. If the vertical axis corresponds to the <u>position</u> of an object, which of the sketches could apply to an object having no acceleration and no initial velocity?

A3. Which of the sketches would describe the <u>position</u> of an object that passes through the origin with a constant, positive velocity?

A4. Which of the sketches would describe the <u>velocity</u> of an object, which is initially at rest, subject to a constant, non-zero acceleration?

A5. Which of the sketches might represent the <u>position</u> of an object whose position was a quadratic function of time?

A6. If the vertical axis corresponds to the <u>velocity</u> of an object, which of the sketches might describe the velocity of an object that was at rest at $t = 0$s?

A7. Which of the sketches could represent the <u>acceleration</u> of an object whose velocity varied linearly with time?

A8. If Sketch E described the <u>position</u> of an object as a function of time, which of the sketches would represent the <u>acceleration</u> of the object?

A9. Which of the sketches would represent the <u>acceleration</u> of an object whose position varied linearly with time?

A10. If Sketch E described the <u>velocity</u> of an object as a function of time, could you determine <u>where</u> the object was located at $t = 0$s? Explain.

A11. Which of the sketches could be used to represent qualitatively the <u>velocity</u> of an object released from rest and allowed to fall in a gravitational field?

A12. If Sketch C described the <u>acceleration</u> of an object, which of the sketches might represent the <u>velocity</u> of the object?

Evaluating Procedures for Solving Kinematics Problems

Purpose and Expected Outcome

This is the first in a set of three activities concerning *procedures* for solving kinematics problems. The first step is to recognize when a particular procedure is valid or invalid.

Prior Experience / Knowledge Needed

You should be able to construct graphs of kinematic quantities vs. time for situations in which the acceleration is constant. Also, you should be familiar with the algebraic expressions for these kinematic quantities. Finally, you should have some experience with word problems within kinematics.

A *procedure*, as we use the term, is a verbal description of the steps needed to solve a word problem. There can be many *valid* procedures for the same problem, as long as the procedure yields the correct answer <u>and</u> as long as each step in the procedure is allowed mathematically and appropriate to the situation. Therefore, if any statement in the procedure is incorrect or inappropriate, then the procedure is not valid.

Explanation of Activity

There are two parts to this activity. In each part you are given different kinematics problems. In the first part, an <u>invalid</u> procedure is presented for each problem. You must find what is wrong with the procedure and explain why the procedure is wrong. In the second part, two procedures are presented for each problem. One of them is valid, and the other in not. You will identify the procedure that is not valid and explain your answer.

Note: You do <u>not</u> need to solve the problems to do this activity.

PART A: Finding What is Wrong with a Procedure

Each of the procedures shown below are <u>not valid</u> for solving the given problem. Explain what is wrong with each procedure.

A1. *Problem:* A child gives a wooden block a push along the floor. When the child releases the block it is moving with a speed 2m/s. If the block slows down with a constant acceleration, what will be the speed of the block after it has moved 1m?

Procedure: The kinematic expression relating the displacement of an object to its speed is:

$$(v_x)^2 = (v_{0x})^2 + 2a_x \Delta x.$$

Since we know the initial speed and the displacement of the block, we can determine its speed after it has traveled 1m.

What is wrong with this procedure?

A2. *Problem:* You are driving down a straight road at 54km/h (15m/s). When you are 30m from a side street, a car abruptly pulls out in front of you and stops. If it takes you 1s to react to the car and if your maximum acceleration is 5m/s², can you stop in time to avoid an accident?

Procedure: (1) Draw a graph of velocity vs. time, starting at 15m/s at t = 0s with a slope of –5m/s², and ending at v_x = 0m/s. (2) Find the area below the velocity vs. time graph between t = 0s and the time at which the velocity is zero. This is your displacement. (3) If your displacement is less than 30m, then the accident is avoided.

What is wrong with this procedure?

A3. *Problem:* You push a block along the floor with an acceleration of 4m/s² for 2s, then you let go of it. The block slows down at a rate of 2m/s² until it stops. What is the average acceleration of the block during this process?

Procedure: We know the initial and final accelerations, 4m/s² and 2m/s², so add them together and divide by two to get the average.

What is wrong with this procedure?

PART B: Selecting the Invalid Procedure

There are three problems to examine in this part. For each problem, two procedures are presented side-by-side. <u>One of them is valid, and the other one is not</u>. (a) Indicate which procedure is not valid and (b) explain why it is not valid.

B1. As you left home one morning, your bus was 20m away and just starting to pull away from the bus stop at 4m/s². You start running at constant speed toward the bus, catching up with it 5s later. How fast did you run?

Procedure I: Draw a graph of the position of the bus as a function of time. It starts out at $x = 20$m and increases with a slope of 4m/s. On the same diagram draw a graph of your position as a function of time, starting at $x = 0$m and going in a straight line to the point representing the position of the bus at $t = 5$s. (See diagram below.) The slope of your position vs. time graph is the speed you ran to catch the bus.

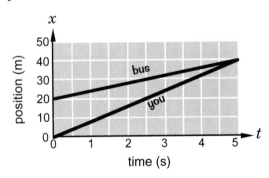

Procedure II: Assuming you start at $x = 0$m, your position as a function of time is:

$$x_A = v_A t$$

where v_A is your speed, which is constant. The bus undergoes constant acceleration, so its position as a function of time is:

$$x_B = x_0 + v_{0x}t + \frac{1}{2}a_x t^2$$

where x_0 is 20m, v_{0x} is zero, and a_x is constant at 4m/s². At $t = 5$s, both you and the bus have the same position, so set $x_A = x_B$. The only unknown in the equation is v_A, so solve for it. This is the speed you ran to catch the bus.

(a) Which procedure is <u>not</u> valid?

(b) Why is this procedure not valid?

continued

B2. Your little sister is playing with a toy car. She winds it up and lets it go. The car speeds up at a constant rate for 2s, then slows down at the same rate (also for 2 seconds) until it stops 3 meters away. What was the acceleration of the toy car for the first 2 seconds of its motion?

Procedure I: Draw a graph of the velocity of the toy car vs. time. The graph starts out at zero and increases to a maximum of v at $t = 2$s, then decreases back to zero at $t = 4$s. (See diagram.) The area below this graph is the displacement of the car, which is 3m. So, equate the area below the graph to 3m, and solve for the unknown speed v. The slope of the velocity vs. time graph is the acceleration.

Procedure II: The acceleration of the toy car is constant and the same for the entire motion of the car. The whole process takes 4 seconds, and the displacement is 3 meters, so use the formula:

$$\Delta x = v_{0x}t + \frac{1}{2}a_x t^2$$

where v_{0x} is zero, Δx is 3m, and t is 4s. The only unknown in the equation is the acceleration a_x, so solve for it.

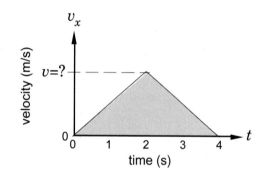

(a) Which procedure is <u>not</u> valid?

(b) Why is this procedure not valid?

continued

B3. A bicyclist is approaching an intersection traveling at 8m/s. Just ahead of the bicyclist, a car is stopped at a red light. When the bicyclist is next to the car, the light turns green, so she continues as before, passing the car. Meanwhile, the car accelerates at a rate of 4m/s^2 until it reaches a cruising speed of 16m/s. At what time (other than $t = 0$s) are the car and the bicyclist next to each other?

Procedure I: Draw graphs of the positions of both the car and bicyclist versus time. When the two graphs intersect, the car and bicyclist are side-by-side.

For the car, the graph starts at $x = 0$m and increases according to the equation $x_C = (2m/s^2)t^2$ until $t = 4$s. After $t = 4$s, it is a straight line with a slope of 16m/s.

For the bicyclist, the graph also starts at $x = 0$m, but increases linearly (instead of quadratically) with a slope of 8m/s.

The time at which these two curves intersect is the time at which the car and the bicyclist are side-by-side. If necessary, check the answer using equations.

Procedure II: The velocity of the car is increasing linearly with time according to:

$$v_C = a_x t,$$

since the car starts out at zero velocity, and its acceleration is constant. As soon as the car reaches a speed of 8m/s, it will be next to the bicyclist. So, use a value of 4m/s^2 for the acceleration a_x and solve for the time t at which v_C is equal to 8m/s. This is the time at which the car and the bicyclist are side-by-side.

(a) Which procedure is _not_ valid?

(b) Why is this procedure not valid?

Reflection

R1. What is the hardest part of comparing two procedures? Explain.

R2. Which type of procedure (graphical or algebraic) was easier to understand? Explain.

Executing Procedures for Solving Kinematics Problems

Purpose and Expected Outcome

This is the second in a set of three activities designed to show you how to create your own procedures for solving problems. After doing this activity, you will have a better sense of how the procedure is related to the solution of a problem. You will also understand better what makes a procedure valid or invalid.

Prior Experience / Knowledge Needed

You should be familiar with *procedures* (a verbal description of the steps needed to solve a problem). You should also be very familiar with graphs of linear (straight line) and quadratic (parabolic) functions. Finally, you should now know the expressions for position and velocity of an object undergoing constant acceleration. In particular, you should know the proper use of the expressions, $x = x_0 + v_{0x}t + \frac{1}{2}a_x t^2$ and $v_x = v_{0x} + a_x t$.

Explanation of Activity

You will be given three kinematics word problems, each with an accompanying procedure. For each problem, decide if the accompanying procedure is valid, and if not, fix it. Then, execute the valid procedure to solve the problem.

A1. A toy car is pushed so that it accelerates at 2m/s^2 for 1.5s, then slows down at 1m/s^2 until it stops What are (a) the maximum speed of the toy car, (b) the time it takes to slow down and stop, and (c) the total distance traveled by the car?

Procedure: Draw a graph of the velocity vs. time for the toy car. It should start at zero and increase linearly for 1.5s with a slope of 2m/s^2. Then the graph should decrease linearly with a slope of –1m/s^2 until it reaches zero again. The maximum speed can be read directly from the graph. The time at which the car stops can also be read directly from the graph, and this can be used to find the time it takes for the toy car to stop. The total distance traveled by the toy car is the area below this graph.

A2. A ball is dropped from an unknown height, accelerating at approximately 10m/s^2 until it hits the ground 2s later. After hitting the ground the ball rebounds at half the speed it had just prior to hitting the ground. (a) When does the ball first come to rest after hitting the ground? (b) How high does the ball rebound?

Procedure: Draw a velocity vs. time graph for the ball. The graph should start at zero and decrease linearly with a slope of –10m/s^2 for 2s. Assuming the impact with the ground takes a negligible amount of time, the graph continues with a <u>positive</u> velocity, starting at $t = 2$s with a value half as large as the velocity just before impact. The velocity again decreases linearly with a slope of –10m/s^2 until it reaches zero. The time at which the velocity is zero (again) is the time that the ball first comes to rest after hitting the ground (part a). The rebound height (part b) is the area below the velocity graph between $t = 2$s and the time the ball first comes to rest.

A3. A ball is rolling up an inclined plane with a constant acceleration. A mark on the incline is used to represent the origin ($x = 0$cm). The ball is observed to be at the origin at $t = 0$s, then 20cm past the origin at $t = 1$s. The ball stops and reverses direction, speeding up and eventually passing the origin. At $t = 4$s, the ball is observed to be 80cm past the origin. (a) What is the acceleration of the ball? (b) At what time does the ball stop before rolling back down the incline?

Procedure: The ball's position as a function of time is given by $x(t) = x_0 + v_{0x}t + \frac{1}{2}a_xt^2$. This equation is valid because the acceleration of the ball is constant and the same for the entire motion of the ball. We know the position at 3 different times so we can solve for the 3 unknowns: x_0, v_{0x}, and a_x. We know that $x = 0$cm at $t = 0$s, so we know x_0. If we set $x = 20$cm at $t = 1$s and $x = 80$cm at $t = 4$s, we have two equations and two remaining unknowns, v_{0x} and a_x. Solve the first equation for v_{0x} and insert the expression for v_{0x} into the other equation. Now the second equation depends only on a_x. Solve for it. This is the answer to part (a).

The expression for the ball's velocity as a function of time is $v_x(t) = v_{0x} + a_xt$. We know the value of a_x from the previous part, but we do not yet know v_{0x}. However, we did just derive an equation for v_{0x} in terms of a_x, so use it to solve for v_{0x}. The time at which the ball stops rolling is the time at which v_x is zero, so set the velocity equal to zero and solve for t. This is the answer to part (b).

Generating Procedures for Solving Kinematics Problems

Purpose and Expected Outcome

This is the third and last activity specifically targeting how to write procedures for solving problems. At the end of this activity, you should be able to create your own procedures. Also you will be able to analyze and discuss with your teacher and with other students <u>how</u> to solve problems.

Prior Experience / Knowledge Needed

You should be familiar with procedures for solving kinematics problems.

Explanation of Activity

For each of the following problems, describe how you would solve it. For example, indicate whether you would use graphs, equations, or both. Which graphs would you use? Which equations? Do you have enough given information to answer all the questions asked? What steps would you follow to answer each question asked?

As a guide to the style of a proper procedure, use the valid procedures previously presented in Activities 31 and 32. Each of your procedures should be complete enough to allow another student to solve the problem by following it.

Note: You are <u>not</u> required to solve the problems in this activity.

A1. The space shuttle Kinematica is 1300m away from the dock of a space station and approaching at 160m/s. The shuttle pilot can give the shuttle a constant acceleration by firing the engines. What constant acceleration should she set so that the shuttle comes to rest right at the dock?

continued

A2. A truck and a sports car are side-by-side at one end of a long straight road. The truck starts from rest at $t = 0$s and accelerates at 1.5m/s^2. The sports car starts from rest at $t = 8$s and accelerates at 3.5m/s^2.

(a) At what time is the sports car's speed equal to the truck's?

(b) What is that speed?

A3. You and your friend are talking on the sidewalk. When you are finished talking she starts walking home at 2.2m/s, and you start riding your bike at 4.0m/s in the opposite direction. Ten seconds later, you realize you forgot to tell her something, so you reverse direction and ride at 6.0m/s towards her.

(a) How long does it take to catch up to your friend?

(b) Where is she at that time?

A4. An accident nearly occurred this morning near the hospital. A car was driving along, and the driver did not see a pedestrian crossing the road until it was almost too late. He slammed on the brakes sliding to a stop 2m from the pedestrian, creating a skid mark 15.2m long.

(a) If speed limit near the hospital is 20mi/h and the maximum acceleration possible for the car is 6m/s^2, was the driver speeding or not?

(b) How fast was he going just before applying the brakes?

Reflection

R1. Is it easier to identify an invalid procedure when the procedure involves graphs or when it involves equations? Explain.

R2. What is the hardest part of using procedures?

R3. Consider the problems in the last few activities. How hard do you think these problems are? Does thinking about a problem's procedure make the problem seem harder for you to solve or easier for you to solve? Explain.

R4. (a) In what ways are graphs better than equations for describing the motion of an object?

(b) In what ways are graphs worse than equations?

Solving Constant-Acceleration Problems

Purpose and Expected Outcome

The purpose of this activity is to develop your ability to choose the best representation in which to solve a constant-acceleration kinematics problem. You have had some experience using strobe diagrams, graphs, and algebraic equation manipulation to solve such problems; now you should practice choosing which representation to use when you have a problem you want to solve.

Prior Experience / Knowledge Needed

You should be thoroughly familiar with graphs of kinematic quantities vs. time, as well as strobe diagrams and the proper use of kinematic equations for constant-acceleration motion. Preferably, you should be equally comfortable with each form so that you can choose the one that solves the problem the easiest.

Explanation of Activity

Each problem presents you with a situation and one or more questions about that situation. Use the method of your choice—using a strobe diagram, manipulation of algebraic equations, or graphing—to answer the questions. Be warned: some questions are much simpler by one method than by others. If you find you are having trouble with a problem, try a different method.

A1. The space shuttle Kinematica is 1300m away from the dock of a space station and approaching at 160m/s. The shuttle pilot can give the shuttle a constant acceleration by firing the engines. What constant acceleration should she set so that the shuttle comes to rest right at the dock?

continued

A2. A truck and a sports car are side-by-side at one end of a long straight road. The truck starts from rest at $t = 0$s and accelerates at 1.5 m/s^2. The sports car starts from rest at $t = 8$s and accelerates at 3.5 m/s^2.

(a) At what time is the sports car's speed equal to the truck's?

(b) What is that speed?

(c) At what time are they side-by-side?

(d) How far have they traveled when they are side-by-side?

A3. You and your friend are talking on the sidewalk. When you are finished talking she starts walking home at 2.2m/s, and you start riding your bike at 4.0m/s in the opposite direction. Ten seconds later, you realize you forgot to tell her something, so you reverse direction and ride at 6.0m/s towards her.

(a) How long does it take to catch up to your friend?

(b) Where is she at that time?

A4. An accident nearly occurred this morning near the hospital. A car was driving along, and the driver did not see a pedestrian crossing the road until it was almost too late. He slammed on the brakes sliding to a stop 2m from the pedestrian, creating a skid mark 15.2m long.

(a) If speed limit near the hospital is 20mi/h and the maximum acceleration possible for the car is 6m/s^2, was the driver speeding or not?

(b) How fast was the driver going just before applying the brakes?

(c) If the driver had reacted a little too late, he would have hit the pedestrian. How much more time did the driver have to react <u>without</u> hitting the pedestrian?

A5. The space shuttle Kinematica is in trouble. It is 2400m away from the dock of a space station and approaching at 120m/s. The engines are malfunctioning, so the pilot can only give the shuttle an acceleration of <u>exactly</u> 20m/s^2 by firing the engines at any time, and she only has enough fuel to fire the engines for a total of 10 seconds.

(a) At what times and for how long should the pilot fire the shuttle's engines so that the shuttle comes to rest right at the dock?

(b) Where is the shuttle when she starts to fire the engines?

Reflection

R1. How did you decide which method to use to solve a problem?

R2. Is sketching a graph useful even if you do not solve the problem using the graph? Explain.

R3. Is sketching a strobe diagram or any other type of diagram helpful even if you do not use it to solve the problem? Explain.

R4. What other types of diagrams might be useful for solving problems?

Summarizing and Structuring Kinematics Ideas

Purpose and Expected Outcome

Now that you have finished learning all the concepts associated with motion, it is a good opportunity to organize them. In this activity, you will become more aware of the properties of kinematic quantities and how they are related to each other. This will make it easier to remember them later, when you want to use them to understand a situation better or to solve a problem. You will also start a list of problem-solving skills, tactics, procedures, and strategies. You will return to this list regularly during the course, adding to and modifying your list as you learn more about physics and about solving problems.

Prior Experience / Knowledge Needed

You should know kinematics. You should understand the meaning of graphs of kinematic quantities versus time. You should know the defining relationships for velocity and acceleration, and how to translate from the graph of one quantity versus time to the graph of another. You should have some experience solving kinematics problems.

Explanation of Activity

There are four parts to this activity.

PART A: Summarizing the Kinematic Quantities

Make a table describing all the quantities you have used to understand the motion of an object. Fill in the table as follows:

Column 1: The name of the kinematic quantity, such as *position*, *velocity*, *speed*, etc.

Column 2: The symbol(s) used to represent this quantity in equations and in text

Column 3: A definition of the quantity in words, and if possible, as an equation

Column 4: Properties of the quantity and its relationship(s) to other quantities in the table

QUANTITY	SYMBOL(S)	DEFINITION	PROPERTIES AND OTHER RELATIONSHIPS
⋮			
velocity	...	...	• vector quantity • slope of position versus time graph ⋮
speed	v	magnitude of the velocity of an object; (that is, $v = \lvert \mathbf{v} \rvert$)	• scalar quantity ⋮
⋮			

PART B: Making Comparisons

Compare your table with the tables that your classmates have made. Discuss your entries and descriptions with them. Make additions and modifications to your table as needed or desired.

PART C: Making a Concept Map

Working in a small group or as a class, organize the entries in your table and arrange them into a diagram showing the meanings and relationships that make up all of kinematics. (We sometimes refer to this structure as a *concept map*, because it shows the "relative position" of ideas and the "connections" between ideas.) An example of a partial concept map is shown below. **Note:** You should make your concept map so that it makes sense to you. Do not copy this one.

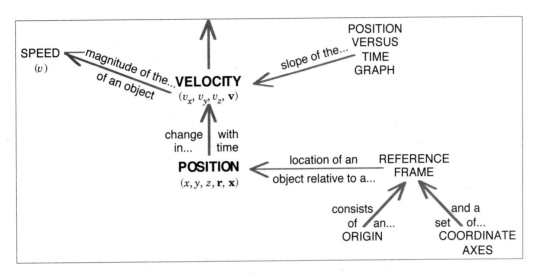

(partial concept map for kinematics ideas)

PART D: Listing Problem-Solving Ideas

As a class, make a list of problem-solving ideas. These include: ways to avoid mistakes, common steps and/or procedures that can be used for different types of problems, tricks for determining a certain quantity, and general strategies for solving problems. Here are some examples:

- Drawing and labeling a sketch of the physical situation helps visualize the situation and reduces the number of errors.

- You must specify an origin or reference point before specifying the position.

- Answers should always be checked to make sure they make sense for the situation.

- A sketch of velocity versus time makes it easy to determine acceleration versus time.

- Make sure you have enough given information to determine the desired unknown.

You might find it useful and helpful to review some of the Reflection questions from the last few activities.

Reader

Chapter 1:
DESCRIBING MOTION

MINDS•ON PHYSICS
READER
CHAPTER 1

DESCRIBING MOTION

Introduction. There are many words from everyday language that we use to describe where objects are and how they move. Consider a few examples:

> The car is traveling at 60 miles per hour.
> The boy walked 2 miles north.
> He lives at 23 Belmont Avenue.
> Mary runs faster than Joe.
> Jane can accelerate her sports car from 0 to 60 miles per hour in 5 seconds.

As you can see from these examples, there are a wide variety of ideas available for describing motion. Is there really a need for a special set of physics ideas to describe motion?

It is not so much that new ideas are needed, but that ideas we already use need to be made more precise. For example, in casual conversation we are likely to mean the same thing by the words "velocity" and "speed." In physics these two terms are used to stand for two different, but related, ideas. Six main terms are used in physics to describe motion: *position*, *displacement*, *speed*, *velocity*, *acceleration*, and *time*.

We start with position, because it is easiest to measure, and because all other motion quantities depend upon it.

1.1 POSITION

Describing the position of an object. The study of motion begins with defining the *position* of an object. The position of something is simply its location relative to some standard or agreed-upon point called the *origin* of the coordinate system. (This should not be confused with the origin of a graph, which is the point at which the axes meet.) The origin used to define the location of an object may also be referred to as the *point of reference*.

Let's begin by considering one-dimensional motion (motion along a straight line). We define a coordinate system by making three choices: a reference point, a unit distance to provide a scale, and a direction taken to be positive. For convenience, let's call the line along which the motion occurs the *x*-axis.

The diagram below shows a rabbit and a turtle located at different positions on the *x*-axis. The reference point is the position $x = 0$. The scale is meters, so each number refers to the number of meters from the reference point. The direction chosen to be positive is to the right, so numbers increase as we go to the right, and become negative as we go to the left.

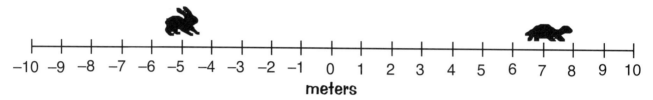

The MKS unit of position is the *meter* (m). One meter is about 39 inches, or about 3 feet and 3 inches. For positions far from the origin, we sometimes use the *kilometer* (km), which is equal to 1000 meters (1000m), and also about 6/10ths of a mile. For small scales, we use the *centimeter* (cm), which is equal to 1/100th of a meter, or about 4/10ths of an inch.

We can specify the position of these two animals in one of several ways. Although we will describe the position of the rabbit and the turtle in three <u>different</u> ways, the information being conveyed is exactly the same. Each of the ways is commonly referred to as a *representation* of the information.

METHOD 1: MAGNITUDE AND DIRECTION REPRESENTATION

The magnitude refers to the distance from the origin and the direction refers to the direction as seen from the origin. For example,

> Position of rabbit =   "5 meters toward the negative direction"
> — or —
> "5m in the negative direction"
>
> Position of turtle =   "7 meters toward the positive direction"
> — or —
> "7m in the positive direction"

You should note that this information is not useful unless we know also the location of the origin, as well as the direction chosen to be positive.

METHOD 2: COMPONENT REPRESENTATION

In this representation, the location is specified by a number with units. The value of the number conveys the distance between the object and the origin, while the sign indicates whether the direction is toward the positive or negative part of the x-axis. For example,

> Position of rabbit = "–5 meters" — or — "–5m"
>
> Position of turtle = "+7 meters" — or — "+7m" — or just — "7m"

As before, to know the actual location of something, we must know the location of the origin and the direction chosen to be positive.

METHOD 3: DIRECTED LINE SEGMENT REPRESENTATION

In this representation, an arrow is used to represent the location relative to the origin. The length of the arrow denotes the distance from the origin and the direction of the arrow indicates the direction of the object relative to the origin. Two examples are shown to the right.

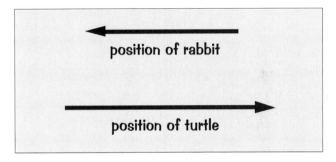

You should note that all three of the methods described above indicate <u>only</u> the location of the object. No other information, such as the orientation (the direction that the rabbit or turtle is facing), is conveyed.

We can generalize these methods to specify the position of an object along two or three dimensions. For example, we can use the three representations to specify the positions of a spider, an ant, and a butterfly in the two-dimensional grid shown to the right.

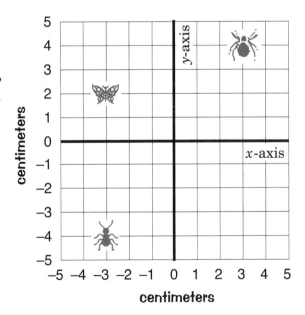

MAGNITUDE AND DIRECTION

The position of the spider is:

5 centimeters in the direction 53° counter-clockwise from the positive x-axis

— or equivalently —

5 centimeters in the direction 37° clockwise from the positive y-axis.

These are shown in the diagrams below:

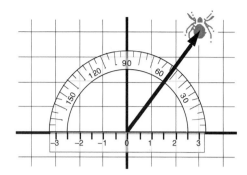 

COMPONENTS

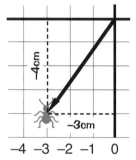

In the component representation, the position of the ant is:

−3 meters along the x-direction,
and −4 meters along the y-direction.

You can see from the diagram that the component representation is like using two number lines, one called the *x*-axis and the other called the *y*-axis. The ant's position is 3cm to the left and 4cm below the origin. So we say that the *x*-component of the position is −3cm, and its *y*-component is −4cm. The minus signs are important, because they indicate that the directions are negative.

DIRECTED LINE SEGMENT

The position of butterfly in the directed line segment representation is the arrow indicated in the picture to the right.

You might wonder why we present three different representations for describing the same thing. When we get to problem solving a little later on, you will see how some problems are very easy to solve in one representation and very difficult to solve in another. Having three different representations provides us with options when we try to solve problems.

Using graphs to describe the position of objects moving in one dimension. One very convenient way to represent the position of an object moving along a straight line is to make a plot or graph of the object's position as it varies with time. For example, the series of pictures to the left shows the position of a marble at different times as it moves along a line.

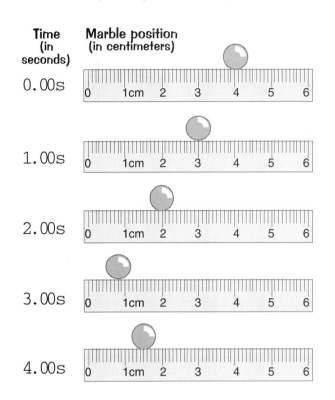

When we make a graph of the information provided by the pictures, we get the graph seen below. This graph shows the position of the marble as it moves with time. At time $t = 1$ second the marble is located at position $x = 3$cm, which means that it is 3 centimeters away from the origin in the positive direction. The marble is 1.5 centimeters from the origin in the positive direction at $t = 4$ seconds, and so forth. (If the marble had been to the left of the origin, <u>negative</u> values would have been needed to indicate its position.)

Both the table and the graph below summarize the data shown in the pictures above.

table of position vs. time data

Position (cm)	Time (s)
4.0	0.0
3.0	1.0
2.0	2.0
0.8	3.0
1.5	4.0

The dashed line connecting the dots in the graph indicates that we do not know with certainty where the marble is located at those times.

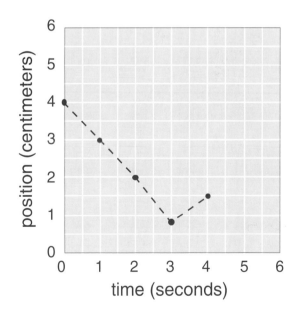

graph of position vs. time

1.2 DISPLACEMENT

We now have a way of describing the position of objects. However, our interest is to describe objects in motion, and objects in motion are constantly changing their positions. We now need a quantity that describes the change in position of moving objects. In physics, the quantity that has proved very useful in describing changes in the position of objects is called *displacement*.

One dimension. The *displacement* is denoted by the symbol Δx (read "delta x") and is defined to be the change in position of an object between two times. (The Greek letter Δ is used in mathematics and physics to mean "the change in." Thus, Δx stands for "the change in x".) We can express the displacement in terms of the position of the object as follows:

$$\Delta x \equiv x(t_2) - x(t_1) = x_2 - x_1 \qquad \text{\textbf{definition of displacement}}$$

The symbols $x(t_1)$ and x_1 <u>both</u> mean the position at time t_1. The above expression, therefore, just means that the change in position of the object between times t_1 and t_2 is the difference between the position of the object at time t_2 and the position of the object at time t_1. For example, from the graph above, the displacement of the marble between times $t = 1$s and $t = 3$s, is $\Delta x = x_2 - x_1 = 0.8$cm $- 3$cm $= -2.2$cm. A positive displacement indicates motion in the positive x-direction, and a negative displacement indicates motion in the negative x-direction.

As another example, consider the diagram below, which represents the position of an airplane at one-second intervals as it lands on a runway. We start our clock when the plane's wheels first touch the ground at 240 meters from our point of reference.

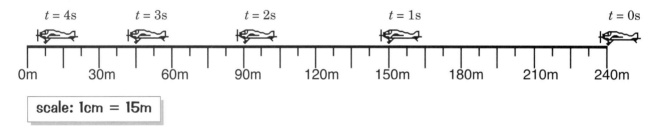

position of an airplane at one-second time intervals

The plane's displacement between times $t = 1$s and $t = 3$s is

$$\Delta x = x(t = 3\text{s}) - x(t = 1\text{s}) = 45\text{m} - 150\text{m} = -105\text{m},$$

where the minus sign indicates that the plane is moving toward the negative direction.

As with position we can represent this displacement in three different ways. In the previous example, expressing the displacement of the plane as −105m used the component representation. We could have expressed this displacement using the other two representations as follows.

In the magnitude and direction representation:

"105 meters to the left"

—or—

"105 meters in the negative x-direction"

In directed line segment representation, the length of the arrow depends on the *scale*. For example, using the same scale that was used above (1cm = 15m), we get an arrow that is 7cm long:

scale: 1cm = 15m

———(7cm long) ———→

But using a scale of 1cm = 30m, <u>the same displacement</u> looks very different. It is only 3.5cm long:

scale: 1cm = 30m

←——(3.5cm long) —→

Displacement in two dimensions. Any of the three representations can be used to describe displacements in two or three dimensions. For example, consider the diagram below, which represents the motion of a car on a three-hour trip. The car starts at the position labeled 3:00pm and moves along a path indicated by the dashed line, arriving finally at the position labeled 6:00pm.

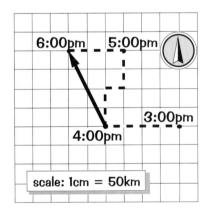

**path of a car
during a 3-hour trip**

We can use all three representations to describe the motion of the car between 4pm and 6pm. In the diagram we have already drawn in the directed line segment for this displacement. It is 2.2cm long, and it points about 27° west of north, so as a magnitude and a direction, we describe the motion of the car as follows:

"Between 4pm and 6pm, the car undergoes a displacement of 110km in a direction 27° west of north."

— or equivalently —

"Between 4pm and 6pm, the car undergoes a displacement of 110km in a direction 63° north of west."

Note that this is <u>not</u> the total distance traveled between 4pm and 6pm. The car actually travels 200km in those two hours, but the displacement depends <u>only</u> on the starting and ending positions of the car during the time interval. Using components, the motion of the car is written:

"Between 4pm and 6pm, the displacement of the car is 50km west and 100km north."

1.3 VELOCITY

Introduction. In the last section the idea of displacement was introduced to describe the change in an object's position. Most of the time we are interested not only in whether an object's position changes, but also in how quickly the position changes. *Speed* is a measure of how much distance an object is traveling per unit time. A car moving with a speed of 80 kilometers per hour travels a longer distance in one second than one moving at 50 kilometers per hour. Note that the speed of an object says nothing about the direction in which the object moves. In physics, we are often interested in <u>both</u> the speed of an object <u>and</u> the direction in which it moves. *Velocity* is the physics quantity that describes both the speed and direction of an object's motion. For example, "50 miles per hour north" is a velocity since it tells us both the speed of the car and the direction in which it is moving.

A practical method for determining whether or not an object has a velocity is to determine if the object is changing its position during some time interval; if the object's position is changing then it has a velocity. To be more precise, consider the following situation: You are given a series of photographs of a marble rolling across a surface in front of a meter stick. Suppose you are first given only two photographs, the second one taken 2 seconds after the first. For example, these photos might look like the following.

At $t = 4.00$s, the marble is 50cm from the left end of the meter stick, and at $t = 6.00$s, it is 80cm from the left end of the meter stick. Therefore it moved 30cm to the right in 2 seconds, so you might say it is moving at 15cm/s.

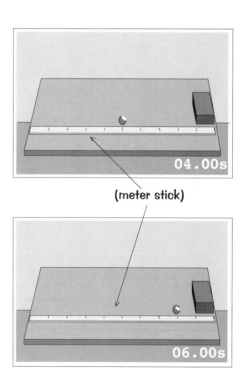

(meter stick)

This description agrees with the photographs, but it assumes that the marble always moves to the right and that its speed is always 15cm/s. Imagine what the pictures might look like if the marble travels at 25cm/s. It would bounce off the brick located at the right end of the table, and would be traveling to the left at the instant the picture was taken. The two pictures would be the same, and there is no way to tell what direction the marble is traveling.

We can say, however, that the displacement of the marble is 30cm to the right during this two-second time interval, and that the *average velocity* is 15cm/s to the right, even though it is not necessarily ever moving at that speed. The definition of average velocity in one dimension is:

$$v_{x,\text{ave}} \equiv \frac{\text{displacement}}{\text{time interval}} = \frac{\Delta x}{\Delta t} = \frac{x(t_2) - x(t_1)}{t_2 - t_1} = \frac{x_2 - x_1}{t_2 - t_1}$$

definition of average velocity

where $x(t_1)$ and x_1 each means the position of the object at time t_1. Note that we have used the definition of displacement (Δx) to write the average velocity.

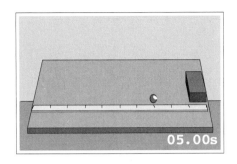

05.00s

Suppose now you are given a third photograph, showing the position of the marble at $t = 5.00$s. The average velocity for the first one-second time interval is 20cm/s to the right:

$$v_{x,\text{ave}} = \frac{\Delta x}{\Delta t} = \frac{x_2 - x_1}{t_2 - t_1} = \frac{70\text{cm} - 50\text{cm}}{5\text{s} - 4\text{s}} = +20\text{cm/s}$$

and for the next 1-second interval, it is –10cm/s. Note that we still do not know where the marble is located at those times between when the pictures were taken.

Sometimes we want to describe the motion of an object at a particular instant. For this we use the *instantaneous velocity* (or simply the *velocity*). When an object is traveling at constant speed and direction, the average velocity over <u>any</u> time interval is equal to the instantaneous velocity during the interval. Therefore, to estimate the velocity of something, we imagine a very small time interval—an interval so small that the speed and direction of motion are the same during the entire interval. The average velocity for this tiny time interval is equal to the instantaneous velocity throughout this same interval. Mathematically, we write it like this:

$$v_x \equiv \frac{\Delta x}{\Delta t} \quad (\Delta t \text{ very small})$$

definition of instantaneous velocity

Note that the direction of motion is determined by the direction of the displacement. If Δx is to the right, then v_x is to the right also.

We can now define the *speed* using the velocity:

$$v \equiv \left| v_x \right|$$

definition of speed

In other words, the speed is the absolute value, or magnitude, of the velocity. It is always positive, and it has no direction associated with it. It merely indicates how fast something moves.

Representing velocity (in two dimensions). Just as for position and displacement, we can describe the velocity in all three representations. To illustrate these, consider the situation on the next page, in which a race car is traveling around a 2km track at a constant speed of 180km/h (50m/s). We assume that time $t = 0$s occurs when the car is at its southernmost position.

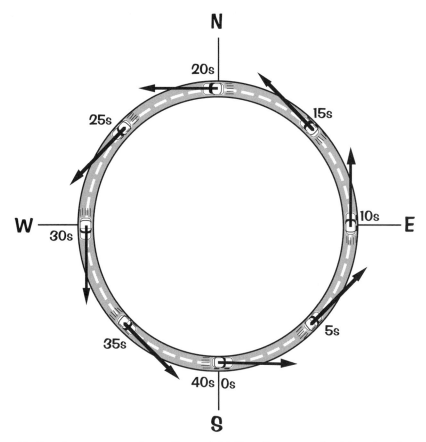

Path of a race car traveling at 180km/h around a 2km track.
Arrows indicate the direction of motion of the race car every 5s.

Because the race car travels 50 meters during every second, it takes 40 seconds to complete one lap (2000 meters). At t = 10s, the car has traveled 500m, so it is 1/4 of the way around the track. The table below shows the car's velocity at this time in each of the three representations. Note that the car is moving in two dimensions, so the velocity has two components.

table showing the velocity of the race car at t = 10s in three representations

Magnitude & Direction	Component	Directed Line Segment
180km/h, north	v_x = 0km/h (east) v_y = 180km/h (north)	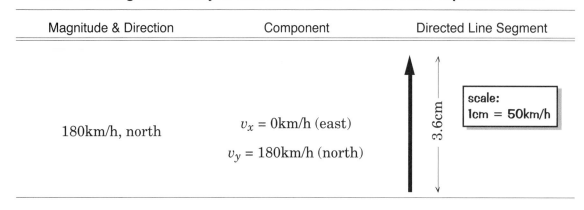

How would we represent the velocity of the race car at $t = 25$s? It turns out that it is quite easy to use either a directed line segment or a magnitude & direction, but it is tricky to use components. The table below shows two of the three results.

velocity of the race car at t = 25s
in two of three representations

Magnitude & Direction	Component	Directed Line Segment
180km/h, 45° south of west	$v_x = -???$ (east) $v_y = -???$ (north)	3.6cm scale: 1cm = 50km/h

The minus signs on the components indicate that they are negative, but without trigonometry we cannot determine their exact sizes. However, by measuring the components of the directed line segment (2.5cm left, 2.5cm down), and converting the distances into km/h using the given scale, we can estimate the velocity at this instant to be about (–125km/h east, –125km/h north) = (125km/h west, 125km/h south). This is shown in the following diagram:

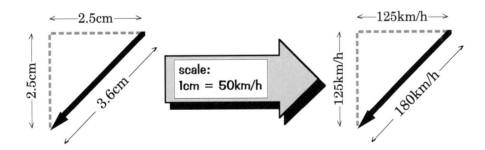

Representing velocity at different times (in one dimension). Plots of velocity versus time are among the most useful and powerful problem-solving tools in physics. We can use them to find displacement as well as acceleration. In this section we will consider three types of motion: motion in which the velocity is constant and positive (car A), motion in which the velocity is constant and negative (car B), and motion in which the velocity is changing with time (car C). Graphs of velocity vs. time are shown below.

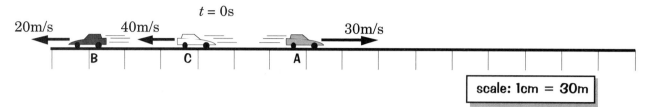

Car A travels at a constant velocity of 30m/s in the positive direction (to the right) during the entire 8-second time interval. Car B travels at a constant velocity of 20m/s in the negative direction (that is, to the left). Car C is initially traveling at 40m/s to the left, but slowing down, so that at $t = 4$s, it stops. It then starts going to the right, speeding up to 40m/s at $t = 8$s. Note that at $t = 2$s, cars B and C have the same velocity, and at $t = 7$s, cars A and C have the same velocity.

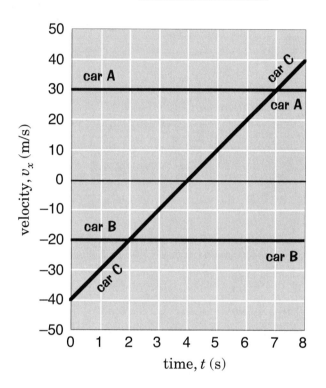

> **At what times do cars A and C have the same speed?**
>
> **Answer.** At $t = 1$s and again $t = 7$s, both A and C are going 30m/s.
>
> **At what times do cars B and C have the same speed?**
>
> **Answer.** At $t = 2$s and again at $t = 6$s, both B and C are going 20m/s.

Relationships between graphs of position and velocity. There are two important relationships between graphs of position and velocity vs. time. To determine what they are, we will consider all three cars, one at a time.

CONSTANT, POSITIVE VELOCITY

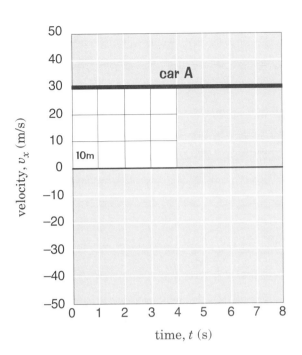

Consider car A from the previous example. Its velocity is constant at 30m/s in the positive direction. (See diagram.) This means that every second, car A moves 30 meters to the right, so compared to where it was at $t = 0$s, it has moved 30m after 1s, 60m after 2s, etc. We do not know where it is located (there is no origin labeled in the previous diagram), but when we know its velocity we know how far it has moved. This is what we have already defined as displacement.

When the velocity is constant, the displacement Δx is represented by the area between the velocity graph and the horizontal (time) axis. This is shown by the 12 white squares in the figure. Each square has an area of $(10\text{m/s} \times 1\text{s}) = 10\text{m}$. So after one second, car A has moved 30m to the right, after 2 seconds, it has moved 60m to the right, etc.

CONSTANT, NEGATIVE VELOCITY

Consider car B from before. Its velocity is constant also, except that it is going only 20m/s and it is going in the negative direction (to the left). Every second, car B travels 20m to the left, so after 1 second, its displacement is –20m, after 2 seconds, its displacement is –40m, and so on.

As before, the displacement is represented by the area between the velocity graph and the time axis. Because the velocity graph is negative, the area is taken to be negative also, so each square has an area of –10m.

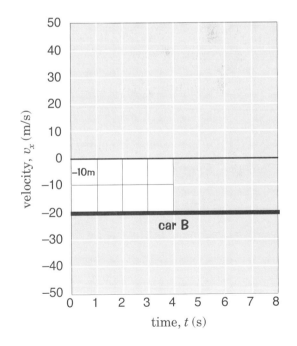

> **What is the displacement of car B between $t = 0$s and $t = 4$s.**
>
> **Answer.** The area shown is –80m, so the displacement is 80m to the left.

CHANGING VELOCITY

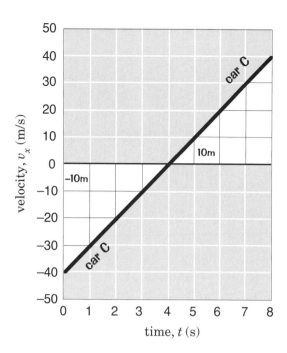

Consider car C from the previous example. Its velocity is changing throughout the 8-second time interval. To relate the velocity and displacement, we imagine very short time intervals—intervals so short that the velocity is nearly constant throughout the time interval. The displacement during each tiny time interval is still the area between the velocity graph and the time axis, and successive displacements are simply added to find the total displacement. So we add these areas to get the total area, which is equal to the total displacement, <u>even when the velocity is not constant</u>.

During the first second, the area is $3\frac{1}{2}$ white squares, each having an area of -10m, so car C moves 35m in the negative direction. During the next second, it moves 25m, and so on. During the first 4 seconds, the displacement is the area of the triangle shown in the figure, which is $\frac{1}{2}(4\text{s})(-40\text{m/s}) = -80\text{m}$. Car C moves 80m to the left during the first four seconds.

What is the displacement of car C between $t = 0$s and $t = 8$s?

Answer. The displacement of car C is the total area shown in the diagram above. For the first four seconds the area is negative, because the velocity is negative, and for the last four seconds the area is positive, because the velocity is positive. The sizes of the two triangles are equal, so their areas add to zero (because one of them has a negative area). Therefore, the displacement of car C during the entire 8s time interval is zero.

Where is car C located at $t = 8$s?

Answer. We do not know where car C is located, but because its displacement is zero, we know that it has returned to its starting position.

Therefore, given <u>any</u> velocity vs. time graph:

> The area below velocity vs. time during any particular time period is equal to the displacement of the object during the same time period.

Let's now choose an origin (O), and look at position vs. time for both cars. As shown below, initially, car A is located at $x = -30$m, car B is located at $x = -210$m, and car C is at $x = -120$m.

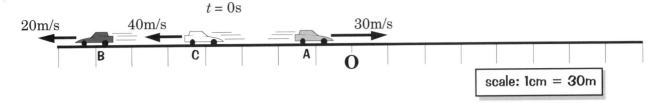

Car A is moving at a constant velocity of 30m/s to the right. This means that each second the car's displacement is +30m, so at $t = 1$s, the car is located at the origin (O); at $t = 2$s, it has moved to $x = 30$m, etc. After 8 seconds, it has moved 240m, so it is located at $x = 210$m. So, constant velocity motion is represented by a straight line on the position vs. time graph.

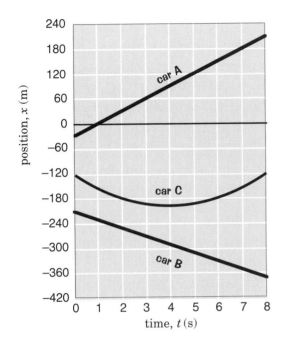

The slope of this line is:

$$\text{slope} = \frac{\text{rise}}{\text{run}} = \frac{240\text{m}}{8\text{s}} = 30\text{m/s}$$

This is the velocity of car A! The reason is that for any two points on the graph, the "rise" is equal to the change in position Δx, and the "run" is equal to the duration of the time interval Δt. So the "rise" divided by the "run" is simply $\Delta x / \Delta t$ which is the definition of average velocity. When the graph is a straight line, the velocity is constant and equal to the average velocity over any time period.

What if the slope of position vs. time is negative? Car B has a constant negative velocity of −20m/s, and the graph of x vs. t is a straight line with a slope of −20m/s. Therefore, even when the slope of position vs. time is negative, it is equal to the velocity.

What if the velocity is changing? When the graph of position vs. time is curved (as for car C), the velocity is changing, so we simply consider very short time intervals—intervals so short that the "curve" looks like a straight line—and determine the slope for a period of time during which the velocity does not change. This is how we defined velocity, so, in all cases:

> The slope of position vs. time at any particular time t
> is equal to the velocity of the object at the same time t.

Note that after $t = 4$s, car C is moving the positive direction, but its position is still negative.

Using algebra to relate position and velocity. When solving problems, we sometimes do not know the time at which something occurs or the velocity or position of something, so we must use symbols to represent them. Even when certain quantities are known, it is often easier to rearrange symbols than to rearrange values. For these and many other reasons, we often use algebra to solve physics problems. In the following example, we show how graphs and algebra are used together to find the desired unknowns.

Joe and his little sister Del are having a race to a tree. Del runs at about 1m/s and Joe runs at 2m/s. If Joe gives Del a 10-second head start, when does Joe catch up to Del?

Answer. Let's draw graphs of position and velocity vs. time for the two people. (This will help us decide how to answer this question.) We have assumed that they are moving in the positive direction, and that they both start at the origin ($x = 0$m).

Joe catches up to Del when they have the same position. This occurs when their position graphs cross, which appears to happen at around $t = 20$s. Let's use algebra to check.

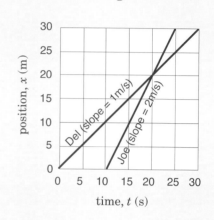

Between $t = 0$s and some time t_1, both have the same displacement. Using the velocity graph, Del's displacement is:

$$\Delta x_{Del} = (1\text{m/s})t_1$$

and Joe's displacement is:

$$\Delta x_{Joe} = (2\text{m/s})(t_1 - 10\text{s})$$

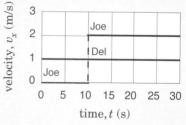

These are equal when $\Delta x_{Joe} = \Delta x_{Del}$, so:

$$(1\text{m/s})t_1 = (2\text{m/s})(t_1 - 10\text{s})$$

This equation is solved by $t_1 = 20$s.

How far have they run at this time?

Answer. Either of the previous relations can be used to find where they are located at $t = 20$s. So:

$$\Delta x_{Del} = (1\text{m/s})(20\text{s}) = 20\text{m}$$

They are at the same position when they are 20 meters from the starting point. This value agrees with the graph of position vs. time: They are both at $x = 20$m at $t = 20$s.

> **If Joe reaches the tree 2 seconds before Del, where is the tree located?**
>
> **Answer.** Again we use the velocity graph to find t_2, the time Joe reaches the tree. Then we use t_2 to find the tree's position.
>
> Their displacements are equal when Del has run for 2s longer than Joe:
>
> $$(1\text{m/s})(t_2 + 2\text{s}) = (2\text{m/s})(t_2 - 10\text{s})$$
>
> This is solved by $t_2 = 22\text{s}$, so the tree is located 24m from the starting point. This can be verified by the graph on the previous page.

In general, when the velocity is constant, the displacement is written:

$$\Delta x = v_x \, \Delta t \qquad\qquad \textbf{displacement for constant velocity}$$

If the initial position is denoted x_0 (that is, at time $t = 0$), then the position of something moving at constant velocity is written:

$$x(t) = x_0 + v_x \, t \qquad \textbf{equation for position vs. time for constant velocity}$$

This is the equation of a straight line having intercept x_0 and slope v_x, which explains why the graph of position vs. time is a straight line when the velocity is constant. It also explains why the slope is equal to the velocity.

We can recover many of our previous relations. For instance, let x_1 = position at $t_1 = x(t_1)$, and x_2 = position at $t_2 = x(t_2)$. Using the lower of the two equations above, we get expressions for x_1 and x_2 as functions of time:

$$x_1 = x_0 + v_x \, t_1$$
and:
$$x_2 = x_0 + v_x \, t_2$$

Subtracting the first equation from the second, we get:

$$x_2 - x_1 = v_x \, (t_2 - t_1)$$

— or simply —

$$\Delta x = v_x \, \Delta t$$

as we have seen many times.

It is important to note that the equations above are valid <u>only</u> when the velocity is constant. When the velocity is not constant, the position vs. time graph becomes curved.

Avoiding pitfalls when working with velocity concepts. Before introducing acceleration, we should discuss some issues that are often confusing. Suppose you take a sight-seeing round-trip with your car between two cities A and B. You choose to travel to B along a winding country road, and then return to A along an interstate highway that is essentially straight. The situation is shown in the diagram to the right. Let's assume that the distance between the two cities along the

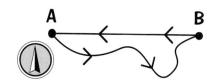

country road is 160km, along the interstate the distance is 120km, and that it takes 4 hours to get to B along the country road, but only 1.2 hours to return to A. If the travelers go at constant speed during each part of the trip, then they go 40km/h along the country road and 100km/h along the interstate. These are their *average speeds* during each part of the trip. The average speed for the whole trip is the total distance divided by the total time:

$$\text{average speed} \equiv \frac{\text{total distance}}{\text{total time}} = \frac{280\text{km}}{5.2\text{h}} = \text{about } 54\text{km/h} \qquad \textbf{definition of average speed}$$

Note that this is <u>not</u> equal to the average of the speeds on the two parts of the trip. This is because the durations of the time intervals for the two parts of the trip are different. This information about the average speed is summarized in the table below.

average speeds for different parts of the trip

Trip	Total distance	Total time	Average speed
A to B	160km	4h	40km/h
B to A	120km	1.2h	100km/h
round trip	280km	5.2h	54km/h

The average velocity during any time interval is found by dividing the displacement during the time interval by the duration of the time interval. So, for the first part of the trip, their average velocity is 30km/h east, <u>not</u> 40km/h east. For the second part, the average velocity is 100km/h west. For the whole trip, the displacement is zero, so the average velocity is zero also. Therefore, the average speed during a trip is equal to the magnitude of the average velocity <u>only when the velocity is constant</u>. These examples are summarized below.

comparison of average velocity and average speed
for different parts of the trip

Trip	Displacement	Time	Average velocity	Average speed
A to B	120km, east	4h	30km/h, east	40km/h
B to A	120km, west	1.2h	100km/h, west	100km/h
round trip	0km	5.2h	0km/h	54km/h

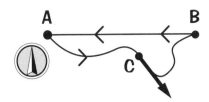

Along the country road, even though the speed is constant, the velocity is constantly changing, because the direction of motion is always changing. For instance, as they pass through town C, the direction is as shown in the diagram. The velocity of the car at this time is therefore 40km/h (speed) at about 60° south of east (direction).

1.4 ACCELERATION

Introduction. *Acceleration* is the physics quantity that describes how slowly or quickly the velocity of an object changes. Like velocity, position, and displacement, acceleration has both a magnitude and a direction. In fact, we will use the same three representations we used before—magnitude & direction, components, and directed line segments.

In common usage, "to accelerate" means "to speed up." This is not true in physics; it means much more than just "to speed up." An acceleration occurs whenever the velocity changes, so if either the speed or the direction of motion changes, then the object undergoes an acceleration. These are the possibilities for what can happen to an object when something else affects its motion. In that case, we say that the other thing exerts a *force* on the object, causing it to accelerate. Later we will explore in greater detail the relationship between the cause of motion—forces—and their effect, as described by an acceleration. This is why the idea of acceleration is so important.

Let's look at four examples of motion and determine if the object in each is accelerating. In the first example, consider a car moving at a constant velocity along a straight road. The diagram below shows the position of the car at equal time intervals. The speedometer reading is constant at about 55 kilometers per hour (15m/s).

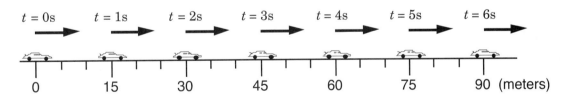

Example 1: A car moving at constant velocity (constant speed and direction)

The directed line segments (one above each car) represent the velocity of the car at the beginning of each time interval. (Speed is designated by the length of the arrow, and direction of motion is designated by the direction of the arrow.) The magnitudes and directions of all the velocities are equal, so there is no change in either the speed or the direction of motion. This means that the car has zero acceleration.

Now consider the diagram below showing another car moving in a straight line along the same road. In this case, the car is going about 115km/h (32m/s) at the beginning, and slows down to about 45km/h (12.5m/s) at the end. Again, directed line segments above the cars represent the velocity of the car at each instant. The lengths of the arrows are changing because the speedometer reading is changing. The direction of motion is not changing, but because the speed is changing, this car is accelerating, <u>even though it is slowing down</u>.

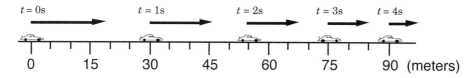

Example 2: A car with changing speed but constant direction

An object also is accelerating when its direction of motion changes, as shown in the next example. A race car moves along a two-kilometer race track at a constant speed of 180km/h. Although the speed is not changing, its direction of motion is always changing as it moves around the track. Therefore, the velocity of the car is changing, and so the car experiences an acceleration.

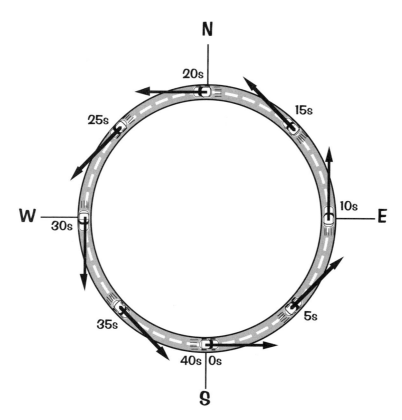

Example 3: A car with constant speed but changing direction

In physics, an object can accelerate even though its speed is constant, as long as the object's direction of motion changes.

As a final example, consider the diagram below showing the trajectory of a thrown ball at equal time intervals. The directed line segments represent the (instantaneous) velocity of the ball at various times. In this example, both the speed and direction of the velocity change, so the ball is accelerating during its trajectory.

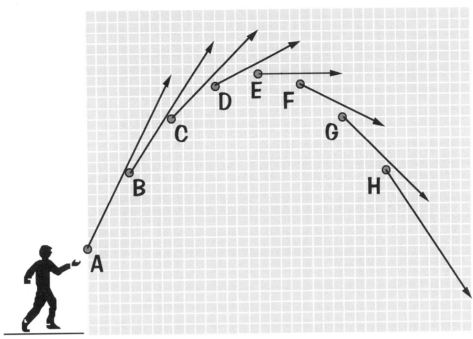

Example 4: A thrown ball has changing speed _and_ direction of motion.

Although it is relatively easy to determine if an object is accelerating by determining whether or not the speed or direction (or both) is changing, it is not as easy to compute the actual value of the acceleration, especially for objects whose velocity is changing direction. We will begin by exploring how to compute acceleration in one dimension, and in a later chapter discuss how to compute the acceleration for objects moving in two and three dimensions.

Defining acceleration for straight-line motion (motion in one dimension). For straight-line motion, we use the symbol x to represent the position of objects and v_x to represent its velocity. Similarly, we use a_x to represent the object's acceleration (in one dimension).

Acceleration is _the rate at which the velocity of an object changes_. To determine how quickly the velocity changes, we must ask how much the velocity changes (Δv_x) and how long the change takes (Δt). Therefore the formal definition of _average acceleration_ over some time interval between t_1 and t_2 requires that we know the velocity at those two times:

$$a_{x,\text{ave}} \equiv \frac{\Delta v_x}{\Delta t} = \frac{v_x(t_2) - v_x(t_1)}{t_2 - t_1} = \frac{v_{2x} - v_{1x}}{t_2 - t_1} \qquad \textbf{definition of average acceleration}$$

where $v_x(t_1)$ and v_{1x} both mean "the velocity at time t_1."

Using this definition of average acceleration for motion along a straight line, the sign of the acceleration determines the direction of the acceleration: a positive acceleration points to the right (or toward larger values of the position, x), while a negative acceleration points to the left (or toward smaller values of the position). Be careful not to confuse the direction of the acceleration with the direction of the motion of the object. Also, you should not assume that the acceleration is negative when the object is slowing down (and positive when it is speeding up). The <u>velocity</u> can increase at the same time that the <u>speed</u> is decreasing (and vice versa). The direction of an object's acceleration depends entirely on how its <u>velocity</u> is changing.

A ball moving to the left with decreasing speed.
Arrows indicate the velocity of the ball at each instant shown.

Let's see how this can happen. Suppose $v_{1x} = -5$cm/s (a ball is moving to the left with a speed of 5cm/s) and $v_{2x} = -2$cm/s measured 2 seconds later. (The ball is now moving to the left at only 2cm/s.) The average acceleration is:

$$a_{x,\text{ave}} = \frac{\Delta v_x}{\Delta t} = \frac{v_{2x} - v_{1x}}{t_2 - t_1} = \frac{-2\text{cm/s} - (-5\text{cm/s})}{2\text{s}} = 1.5\text{cm/s}^2$$

So, the acceleration of the ball is positive, <u>even though its speed is decreasing</u>, because v_x is actually increasing. (Remember, on a number line, –2 is greater than –5.) According to its definition, the acceleration will be positive whenever v_{2x} is greater than v_{1x}. This can occur in only three ways: (1) when an object has a positive velocity and its speed is increasing, (2) when the object has a negative velocity and its speed is decreasing, and (3) when its direction is changing from negative to positive.

Similarly, the acceleration is negative whenever the velocity is changing negatively. This happens (1) when the velocity is positive and the speed is decreasing, (2) when the velocity is negative and the speed is increasing, and (3) when the velocity changes from positive to negative. Some of these results are summarized in the table on the next page.

Direction of motion	Change of speed	Change of velocity	Acceleration	Example
+	+	+	+	
+	−	−	−	
−	+	−	−	
−	−	+	+	

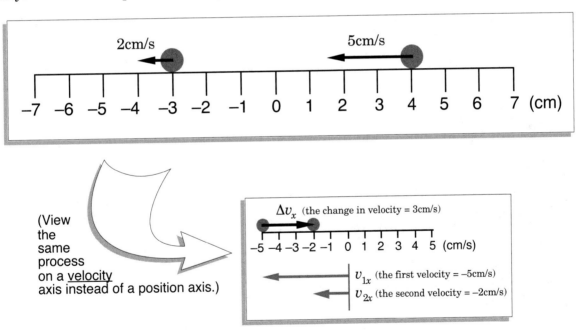

In general, the direction of an object's acceleration is the same as the direction of its change in velocity. Consider the previous example of a ball rolling to the left with decreasing speed:

Note that we have added a second number line, separate from the number line used for position. Its units are cm/s, and it is a number line for <u>velocity</u>. Initially the ball has a velocity of −5cm/s, so there is a ball "located" at −5cm/s on the velocity axis. Two seconds later, the ball has a velocity of −2cm/s, as shown. The change in velocity points "from" the initial velocity "to" the final velocity, so the change in velocity is 3cm/s to the right, as indicated by the black arrow on the lower figure. Therefore, the average acceleration points to the right as well.

As with velocity, we can define an *instantaneous acceleration* (or just *acceleration*) by using very small time intervals—intervals so small that the acceleration does not change during any one of them:

$$a_x \equiv \frac{\Delta v_x}{\Delta t} \quad (\Delta t \text{ very small})$$

definition of acceleration

The idea here is that when we find the average acceleration over a long time interval, we do not know what the acceleration is at any instant during the interval; we only know the overall average. If we want to know what is happening at, say, $t = 10$s, then finding the average from 0s to 20s is <u>not</u> likely to tell us much about what is happening at 10s. But if we find the average acceleration between $t = 9.99$s and $t = 10.01$s, we are much more likely to have an accurate picture. The instantaneous acceleration can be viewed as the value that the average acceleration approaches as we find it for shorter and shorter time intervals containing the instant in question. When the acceleration is <u>constant</u> (that is, it doesn't change with time) the acceleration at each instant during a time interval will equal the average acceleration for the interval. Therefore, if we choose a time interval for which the acceleration does not change <u>too much</u>, then the average acceleration over that time interval is a good estimate of the acceleration during that same time interval.

Representing and interpreting acceleration in one dimension. Acceleration describes changes in velocity. Let's explore the meaning of acceleration, as well as ways of representing it, by considering two examples from before. The diagram below represents a car moving along a straight road. The car's position at one-second time intervals is shown. Above each car, its velocity is represented by a directed line segment. The scale used for velocities is 1cm = 10m/s.

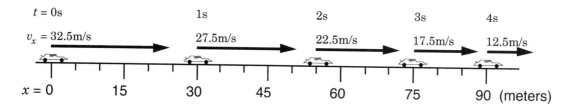

The diagram shows that the length of each directed line segment representing the velocity decreases as the car moves to the right, so the car is accelerating. Notice that during each time interval, the velocity decreases by the same amount (5m/s). Although there may be small fluctuations here and there, it is likely that the acceleration of the car is constant.

Consider the same motion using a number line for <u>velocity</u>:

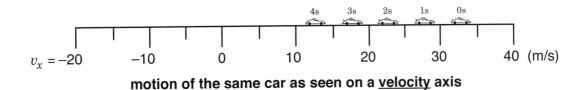

motion of the same car as seen on a velocity axis

If the process continues past t = 4s with the same acceleration, we can see from this diagram that eventually the car will stop (when v_x = 0). In fact, we can predict approximately when this will happen. According to the diagram, the car will stop at some time between t = 6s and t = 7s. Then its velocity will become increasingly negative. In other words, the car will change directions, and its speed will start to increase, <u>even though its acceleration has not changed</u>. The car's acceleration always points to the left!

The acceleration can be represented in all three representations used already for position, displacement, and velocity. So far, we have been using the component representation. Let's look at the acceleration of the most recent example in each representation.

Assuming that the acceleration of the car is constant throughout its motion, we can use any time interval to calculate its acceleration:

$$a_x = a_{x,\text{ave}} = \frac{\Delta v_x}{\Delta t} = \frac{-5\text{m/s}}{1\text{s}} = -5\text{m/s}^2$$

This is the component representation of the acceleration. As a magnitude and direction we say:

"The acceleration of the car is 5m/s² to the left."

And as a directed line segment:

$\longleftarrow$

$\longleftarrow$ 2.5cm $\longrightarrow$

scale: 1cm = 2m/s²

Relationships between graphs of acceleration, velocity, and position (vs. time). We will only consider objects moving with constant acceleration. This means that a graph of acceleration vs. time will be a horizontal line. Just as the graphs of position and velocity were related, the graphs of acceleration, velocity, and position are all interrelated. To illustrate this, consider the following graphs, which represent the position, velocity, and acceleration of a bicyclist who has just started rolling down a steep hill.

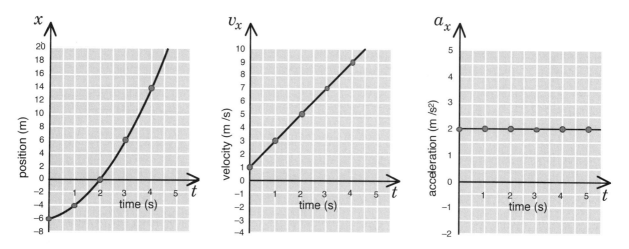

In the section on velocity, we found that the slope of position vs. time at any time is equal to the velocity at the same time. Let's check this result at two different times, $t = 2$s and $t = 4$s.

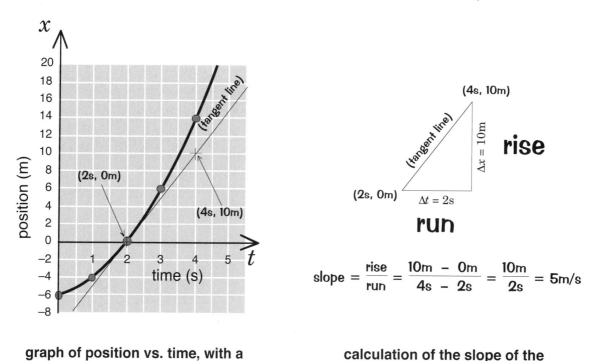

graph of position vs. time, with a
tangent line drawn at time t = 2s

calculation of the slope of the
tangent line at time t = 2s

$$\text{slope} = \frac{\text{rise}}{\text{run}} = \frac{10\text{m} - 0\text{m}}{4\text{s} - 2\text{s}} = \frac{10\text{m}}{2\text{s}} = 5\text{m/s}$$

Note that the slope of the tangent line at $t = 2$s is equal to the velocity at $t = 2$s.

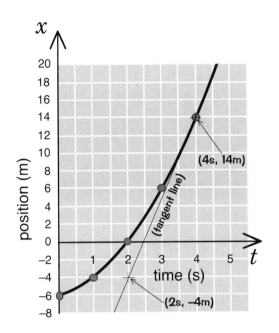

graph of position vs. time, with a tangent line drawn at time t = 4s

calculation of the slope of the tangent line at time t = 4s

$$\text{slope} = \frac{\text{rise}}{\text{run}} = \frac{14m - (-4m)}{4s - 2s} = \frac{18m}{2s} = 9m/s$$

Similarly, the slope of the tangent line at $t = 4$s is equal to the velocity at $t = 4$s.

Let's now look at the slope of the <u>velocity</u> vs. time graph. The graph is a straight line, so its slope is constant and given by:

$$\left(\begin{array}{c}\text{slope of the velocity vs. time graph} \\ \text{between times } t = 0\text{s and } t = 4\text{s}\end{array}\right) = \frac{\text{rise}}{\text{run}} = \frac{9m/s - 1m/s}{4s - 0s} = \frac{8m/s}{4s} = 2m/s^2$$

Note that the slope of velocity vs. time is the acceleration of the bicyclist. This turns out to be always true, even when the acceleration is not constant. The reason is that the "rise" of a velocity vs. time graph is a change in velocity (Δv_x) and the "run" is the duration of a time interval (Δt), so:

$$\text{slope of velocity vs. time} = \frac{\text{rise}}{\text{run}} = \frac{\Delta v_x}{\Delta t} = a_{x,\text{ave}}$$

When the acceleration is constant, this is equal to the instantaneous acceleration at every instant during the time interval. When the acceleration is changing, we take short time intervals—intervals during which the <u>acceleration</u> is roughly constant. This is how we defined acceleration, so, in general:

> The slope of velocity vs. time at any particular time t
> is equal to the acceleration of the object at the same time t.

We can also relate the velocity and acceleration vs. time graphs in another way. When the acceleration is constant, the change in velocity is given by:

$$\Delta v_x = a_x \, \Delta t$$

On a graph of acceleration vs. time, this is the area between the graph and the time axis. So, using the bicyclist again, between $t = 0$s and $t = 4$s, the area below the acceleration curve is:

$$\left(\begin{array}{c} \text{area below } a_x \text{ vs. } t \\ \text{between } t = 0\text{s and } t = 4\text{s} \end{array} \right) = a_x \, \Delta t = \left(2\text{m/s}^2 \right) \times 4\text{s} = 8\text{m/s}$$

Note that this is <u>not</u> the velocity of the bicyclist at $t = 4$s, but the <u>change</u> in velocity between $t = 0$s and $t = 4$s.

When the acceleration is negative, we treat the area as being negative also, so that the change in velocity is negative, as expected.

When the acceleration is changing, we consider short time intervals. The area below the graph during each time interval is the change in velocity during that interval. To find the change in velocity for a large time interval, we simply add up the changes over each short time interval. This means we simply add the areas below each short part of the graph, so the total area is still the change in velocity. In general:

> The area below acceleration vs. time during any particular time period
> is equal to the change in velocity of the object during the same time period.

An acceleration vs. time graph is shown to the right. What is the change in velocity between $t = 0$s and 4s?

Answer. The change in velocity is the area below acceleration vs. time, which is a trapezoidal region of total area 8m/s. The change in velocity is +8m/s.

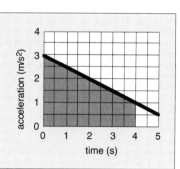

Deriving the kinematic equations for constant acceleration. The relationships between graphs and equations are extremely useful for analyzing physical situations, especially when the acceleration is constant. It is important to keep in mind, however, that each of these equations is derived from the definitions of position, displacement, velocity, and acceleration using graphs. There will be many situations where the equations are <u>not</u> valid, but the method by which they were derived is always valid. Therefore, make sure that you understand the method, and that you can repeat it if necessary later on.

The simplest case is when the acceleration is constant and zero. The velocity is therefore constant also. We notate this constant velocity to be v_{0x}. (We are still in one dimension.) A graph of velocity vs. time is sketched at right. To find the change in position, we calculate the area below velocity vs. time. The preferred starting point is $t = 0s$, and the time interval extends from $t = 0s$ to time t. The area below velocity vs. time during this period is $v_{0x} t$, so this is the <u>change</u> in position between $t = 0s$ and time t. To find the actual position at time t, we add the initial position x_0. This process is shown in the diagram below.

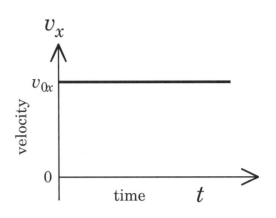

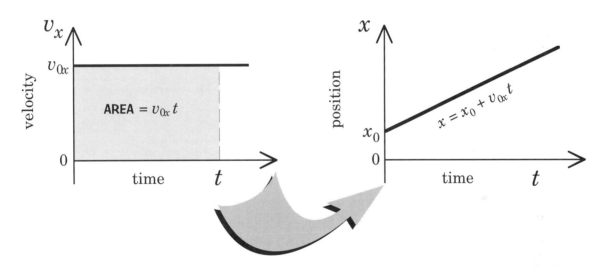

Mathematically, this derivation may be represented as follows.

$$\begin{pmatrix} \text{position } x \\ \text{at time } t \end{pmatrix} = \begin{pmatrix} \text{position } x \\ \text{at time } t = 0s \end{pmatrix} + \begin{pmatrix} \text{change in position} \\ \text{between 0s and time } t \end{pmatrix}$$

$$x(t) = x_0 + \Delta x$$

$$x(t) = x_0 + \begin{pmatrix} \text{area below velocity graph} \\ \text{between 0s and time } t \end{pmatrix}$$

$$x(t) = x_0 + v_{0x} t \qquad \textbf{position at time t for constant velocity}$$

ACCELERATION ≠ 0

For cases when the velocity is steadily varying, the rate at which it is changing is the acceleration. The velocity at time t is found using the graph of acceleration vs. time, as shown below:

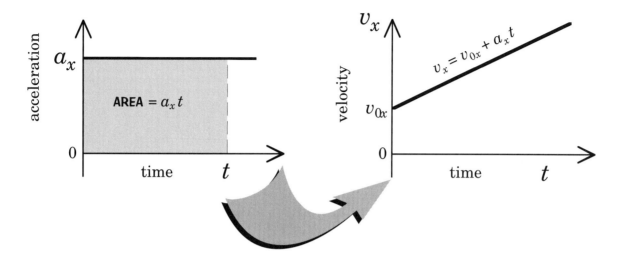

The area below the acceleration vs. time graph is the change in velocity, so:

$$\begin{pmatrix} \text{velocity } v_x \\ \text{at time } t \end{pmatrix} = \begin{pmatrix} \text{velocity } v_x \\ \text{at time } t = 0\text{s} \end{pmatrix} + \begin{pmatrix} \text{change in velocity} \\ \text{between 0s and time } t \end{pmatrix}$$

$$v_x(t) = v_{0x} + \Delta v_x$$

$$v_x(t) = v_{0x} + \begin{pmatrix} \text{area below acceleration graph} \\ \text{between 0s and time } t \end{pmatrix}$$

$$v_x(t) = v_{0x} + a_x t \qquad \textbf{velocity at time t for constant acceleration}$$

This is the equation of a straight line. As shown in the previous diagram, the graph of velocity vs. time is a straight line with a slope equal to the acceleration.

The method for finding the change in position is the same as before. Starting at $t = 0$s, we find the area between the velocity graph and the time axis, as represented on the next page.

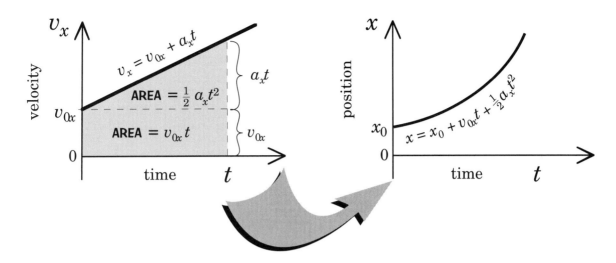

The derivation proceeds as before. Note how we are actually using the graph of velocity vs. time to visualize the terms needed to write out the position.

$$\begin{pmatrix} \text{position } x \\ \text{at time } t \end{pmatrix} = \begin{pmatrix} \text{position } x \\ \text{at time } t = 0\text{s} \end{pmatrix} + \begin{pmatrix} \text{change in position} \\ \text{between 0s and time } t \end{pmatrix}$$

$$x(t) = x_0 + \begin{pmatrix} \text{area below velocity graph} \\ \text{between 0s and time } t \end{pmatrix}$$

$$x(t) = x_0 + \begin{pmatrix} \text{area of rectangular region} \\ \text{between 0s and time } t \end{pmatrix} + \begin{pmatrix} \text{area of triangular region} \\ \text{between 0s and time } t \end{pmatrix}$$

$$x(t) = x_0 + v_{0x}\, t + \frac{1}{2}\, a_x\, t^2 \qquad \textbf{position at time t for constant acceleration}$$

Whenever the position vs. time graph is curved, we know that the slope is changing. Therefore, the velocity is also changing, and the object must be accelerating.

A third equation is derived by solving $v_x(t)$ for the time t and inserting the result into $x(t)$. The result is a relationship between velocity and displacement for constant acceleration:

$$(v_x)^2 = (v_{0x})^2 + 2a_x\, \Delta x \qquad \textbf{squared velocity after displacement } \Delta \textbf{x} \\ \textbf{for constant acceleration}$$

An example will help clarify the meaning of the areas below acceleration vs. time and velocity vs. time.

A dragster accelerates at 15m/s² for 4s, then travels at constant speed for 2s until its parachute opens, causing it to slow down at 10m/s². **(a)** What is the dragster's maximum speed? **(b)** How far has it traveled after 4s? **(c)** after 6s? **(d)** At what time does the dragster stop? **(e)** What total distance has it traveled?

Answer. Let's draw graphs of acceleration and velocity vs. time for the dragster. We assume that all motion is along a straight line, that the initial velocity is zero, and that the initial position is zero. **Note:** After $t = 6$s, the acceleration is negative.

(a) As shown by the velocity vs. time graph, the maximum speed occurs between $t = 4$s and $t = 6$s. The area below acceleration between $t = 0$s and $t = 4$s is $(15\text{m/s}^2) \times (4\text{s}) = 60$m/s, so the maximum speed is 60m/s.

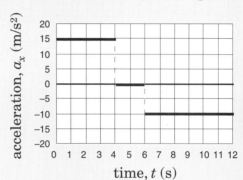

(b) The displacement between $t = 0$s and $t = 4$s is the area of the triangular region below velocity vs. time.

$$\Delta x = \frac{1}{2}(60\text{m/s})(4\text{s}) = 120\text{m}$$

The dragster travels 120m during the first 4 seconds. The acceleration is constant, so this can be verified using:

$$x(t) = x_0 + v_{0x}\, t + \frac{1}{2}\, a_x\, t^2$$

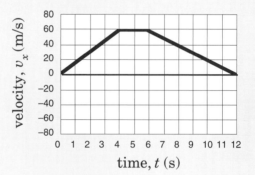

with $x_0 = 0$m, $v_{0x} = 0$m/s, and $a_x = 15\text{m/s}^2$.

(c) The displacement between $t = 4$s and $t = 6$s is $(60\text{m/s})(2\text{s}) = 120$m, so the dragster travels a total of 240m during the first 6s.

(d) After $t = 6$s, the graph of velocity is a straight line with a slope equal to the acceleration (-10m/s^2). The "rise" is 60m/s, so the "run" must be 6 seconds.

$$\Delta v_x = a_x\, \Delta t \quad \Rightarrow \quad \Delta t = \frac{\Delta v_x}{a_x} = \frac{-60\text{m/s}}{-10\text{m/s}^2} = 6\text{s}$$

The dragster stops at $t = 12$s (that is, 12 seconds after it starts).

(continued on the next page)

Answer (continued).

(e) The displacement from $t = 6s$ to $t = 12s$ is the area of the triangular region below velocity vs. time.

$$\Delta x = \tfrac{1}{2}(60\text{m/s})(6\text{s}) = 180\text{m}$$

The dragster travels a total of 420m during the entire 12-second time interval.

(**Note:** This is also the area below the trapezoidal region below velocity vs. time:

$$\Delta x_{\text{total}} = \tfrac{1}{2}(60\text{m/s})(12\text{s} + 2\text{s}) = 420\text{m}.)$$

1.5 KINEMATICS

This is kinematics—the study of the motion of objects. We have defined five motion quantities: position, displacement, velocity, speed, and acceleration. We have shown how they are related and how graphs versus time are related. In this section, we summarize what we have covered so far.

Definitions. Each of the motion quantities has a formal definition. They are repeated in the table below. (**Note:** These definitions are for motion in one dimension.)

Quantity	Symbol	Definition	Mathematical Definition	Comments
POSITION	x	location of an object relative to an origin	(none)	• has both magnitude and direction
DISPLACEMENT	Δx	change in position	$x_2 - x_1$	• has both magnitude and direction
AVERAGE VELOCITY	$v_{x,\text{ave}}$	average rate at which the position is changing	$\dfrac{\Delta x}{\Delta t}$	$= \dfrac{\text{displacement}}{\text{time interval}}$ $= \dfrac{x_2 - x_1}{t_2 - t_1}$
VELOCITY	v_x	rate at which the position is changing	$\dfrac{\Delta x}{\Delta t}$ (Δt small)	• also referred to as the "instantaneous velocity" • speed and direction of motion
SPEED	v	magnitude of the velocity	$\left| v_x \right|$	• no direction
AVERAGE SPEED	v_{ave}	average rate at which the object is moving	$\dfrac{\text{total distance}}{\text{total time}}$	• <u>not</u> equal to the magnitude of the average velocity
AVERAGE ACCELERATION	$a_{x,\text{ave}}$	average rate at which the velocity is changing	$\dfrac{\Delta v_x}{\Delta t}$	$= \dfrac{\text{change in velocity}}{\text{time interval}}$ $= \dfrac{v_{2x} - v_{1x}}{t_2 - t_1}$
ACCELERATION	a_x	rate at which the velocity is changing	$\dfrac{\Delta v_x}{\Delta t}$ (Δt small)	• also referred to as the "instantaneous acceleration" • has both magnitude and direction

Note how each definition needs other definitions in order to express it.

Relationships between graphs of motion quantities. Based on the definitions above, we showed that the slopes of position and velocity vs. time are the velocity and acceleration. We also derived relationships concerning the areas below graphs of velocity and acceleration. These are summarized below.

The slope of a position vs. time graph at any time t is the velocity at the same time t.	The slope of a velocity vs. time graph at any time t is the acceleration at the same time t.
The area below velocity vs. time during any time interval is the change in position during the same time interval.	The area below acceleration vs. time during any time interval is the change in velocity during the same time interval.

Note that velocity is important for each of these. This is why graphs of velocity vs. time are often the most useful, especially when the acceleration is constant.

The following diagram summarizes these four relationships between graphs of motion quantities. Note that the <u>relationships</u> are true *even when the acceleration is not constant*.

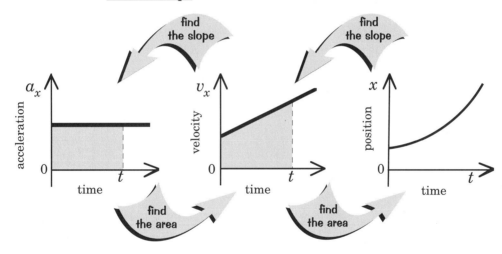

Derived equations relating the motion quantities. Finally, using definitions of motion quantities, along with their graphs vs. time, we derived three equations for motion having constant acceleration. They are:

velocity at time t: $\quad v_x(t) = v_{0x} + a_x t$

position at time t: $\quad x(t) = x_0 + v_{0x}t + \frac{1}{2}a_x t^2$

squared velocity after displacement Δx: $\quad (v_x)^2 = (v_{0x})^2 + 2a_x \Delta x$

$$\text{where:} \quad v_{0x} = \text{initial velocity} = \text{velocity at time } t = 0\text{s}$$
$$a_x = \underline{\text{constant}} \text{ acceleration}$$
$$x_0 = \text{initial position} = \text{position at time } t = 0\text{s}$$

Conclusion. Problem solving is a difficult process. First, you must interpret the problem. You must decide what is given and what is unknown; you must recognize what information may be assumed and what should not be assumed. You must decide what information is relevant and what information is not. You must know all the definitions and how they relate to each other. Finally, you must decide how you will combine these ideas to determine the desired unknown. It turns out that you do <u>not</u> need to memorize any derived equations. Instead, if you know how to graph acceleration and velocity vs. time, and if you know how they are related to changes in velocity and position, then most problems are more easily solved.

As you learn about interactions and forces, we will continue to refer back to kinematics and motion quantities, because <u>forces cannot be observed directly</u>. We come to believe they exist, because forces explain why objects behave the way they do. We can observe directly only position and changes in position. Often we can also estimate velocity; and sometimes we can make certain guesses about acceleration. Therefore, understanding the motion of objects will remain important throughout this course.